W9-BRA-759

Also by Rik Isensee

Fiction:
The God Squad, a spoof on the ex-gay movement. "*. . . brilliantly over the top . . . It's twisted, but it's getting funnier with each page . . . I couldn't help but enjoy this fine display of Rik Isensee's wicked sense of humor. Honest!*" —Jeffrey Jasper, *Lambda Book Report.*

We're Not Alone, a young adult novel dealing with gay, bisexual, and lesbian youth. "We're Not Alone *is fast-paced, well-written, and funny. This book belongs in the library of every high school.*"
—Joyce Hunter, MSW, CSW,
President of the National Lesbian/Gay Health Foundation.

Self-help:
Love Between Men, a guide to resolving conflicts and enhancing intimacy in gay relationships. "*An excellent and very practical guide for making relationships work.*"
—David McWhirter and Andrew Mattison,
co-authors of *The Male Couple.*

Reclaiming Your Life, a guide to recovery from early abuse, homophobia, and self-defeating behavior. "*. . . an indispensable guide for recovery and the development of self-esteem that is the cornerstone for building a self-actualized and happy life.*"
—Michael Shernoff, ACSW,
co-director, Chelsea Psychotherapy Associates.

Are You Ready?, The Gay Man's Guide to Thriving at Midlife. "*. . . an engaging, intimate conversation about how to live with wisdom and passion while embarked on the uncertain journey of midlife.*"
—Robert M. Kertzner, MD, Columbia University.

The Gay Man's Guide to Love and Intimacy (a tape from Sounds True). A guide to developing intimacy through clear communication with your partner.

Plays:
Censored! —A Mocudrama in Two Unnatural Acts.

Hony-Tonk Parade, winner of the James Highsmith Playwriting Award, a prize for new gay plays.

Spank the Monkey

Spank the Monkey

Reports from the Front Lines of Our Quirky Culture

Rik Isensee

Unlimited Publishing
Bloomington, Indiana

Distributing Publisher:
Unlimited Publishing LLC
Bloomington, Indiana

http://www.unlimitedpublishing.com

Contributing Publisher: Rik Isensee

Cover and book design by Charles King. Copyright © 2003 by Unlimited Publishing LLC. This book was typeset with Adobe® InDesign®, using the Minion®, Willow®, Myriad®, and Adobe Jensen® typefaces. This book makes use of one or more typefaces specifically licensed by and customized for the exclusive use of Unlimited Publishing LLC.

First edition.

Copies of this book and others
are available to order online at:

http://www.unlimitedpublishing.com/authors

ISBN 0-7394-4177-9

Unlimited Publishing
Bloomington, Indiana

Library of Congress Cataloging-in-Publication Data

Isensee, Rik
Spank the Monkey—Reports from the Front Lines of Our Quirky Culture / Rik Isensee

p. cm.

1. Humorists, American—21st century. 2. United States—Social Life and Customs—21st century—Humor. 3. Religion—Satire. 4. Homosexuality—Humor. I. Title.

Contents

Spank the Monkey

SAN FRANCISCO: The Save Our Simians subcommittee of the Junior League chapter of the Society for the Protection Of Our Furry Friends (SPOOFF) has denounced the practice, apparently common among gay men, of what is euphemistically called "spanking the monkey." A spokeswoman issued the following statement:

It has come to our attention that a gay bar called The Spunky Monkey sponsors "Spank the Monkey" parties, where men gather in a circle and take turns spanking the spunk out of some poor monkey!

We are aware that a spanking fetish thrives in this community, where "bad boys" are paddled by hunky dads, and while we don't condone corporal punishment, it's one thing for consenting adults to abuse each other, but quite another to beat a blameless monkey!

While we acknowledge there may be aspects of the homosexual lifestyle we don't fully appreciate or understand, it's possible to take cultural relativism much too far! There are standards of decency every member of society must observe. We cannot sit idly by while defenseless animals are being exploited, ill-treated, and brutalized!

Apologists dismiss our concern by claiming "It's all in good fun," or "It's a natural release, especially if you don't have a partner." Not having a partner for your spanking party is no excuse for persecuting this sensitive primate! The unfortunate creature has no conception of being "bad." He can't possibly realize that it's all in sport—all he knows is that he's getting whacked!

Spanking monkeys is not only cruel, it's dangerous! A manhandled monkey is not likely to take this punishment lying down! He could wriggle out of your grasp and bite you! One can't help but wonder whether this abominable ritual is what led to the transmission of AIDS in the first place.

We don't approve of keeping monkeys as pets, but if you have a monkey in captivity, please treat him kindly: hold him snugly, stroke and fondle him with affection, offer him a bite of your banana, but for goodness sake don't abuse him for the amusement of your friends!

We support civil rights for homosexuals, but NEVER at the expense of innocent monkeys! The Save Our Simians subcommittee of the Junior League calls on reasonable members of the gay community to condemn this practice. Monkeys belong in the jungle, not in gay bars! Bang on someone your own size! Stop the abuse, now! FREE THE MONKEYS!

(signed)

—Jane Goodall, Dian Fossey,
and 92 members of the Junior League.

Niagra

NIAGRA, the new potency pill for men, is all the rage. Men are reporting a surge in sexual interest, and love-bird couples are flocking to their favorite falls for a second honeymoon.

Now that men can get it up any time they want, women no longer have to worry about getting them in the mood. Susan Vamp says, "It used to be you had to cajole a man into having sex, convince him that you really loved him, that you wouldn't leave on the next train, or chase after some other guy as soon as you were through with him. You had to win his trust and use romance—candles, flowers, cards—to get him aroused. Not anymore! Now, with Niagra, he pounces on you like an eager puppy, licking his chops, wagging his tail, and humping your leg. Forget foreplay—he's ready to do it right there in the doorway! All these pussy cats have turned into tigers, and I, for one, love it."

Not all women, however, express such delight in their husbands' randy behavior. While it's great that they're finally able to perform, it seems that for a significant percentage of men, that's all they really want to do. They prance about the bedroom, showing off their swollen member and playing with it like a new toy. At the climax of their little show, they fall asleep, leaving the women high and dry (as usual).

An unwelcome side-effect of the drug is a disorienting dizziness. Apparently the rush of blood needed to support their budding tumescence deprives the brain of its usual supply of oxygen. This has led to some strange behavior, as men who would normally never grab or fondle an unwilling woman can no longer restrain their amorous impulses. Once they get an erection, all judgment about appropriate behavior flies out the window. Inexplicably, and without any conscious control, they find themselves humping anything that moves.

A recent well-known case of sexual harassment was thrown out of court when it was determined that the defendant was under the influence of Niagra. "What could I do?" the hapless victim said. "I took this pill, and the whole world started shifting and swirling. I had to clutch onto something just to keep from falling down. Her breast was simply the nearest object. Once I grabbed on, I naturally had to hump her. It was beyond my control—I think it was biological."

Feminist groups are in a tizzy. The last thing they needed was another excuse for wayward behavior in the board room. They're trying to get the new drug restricted to use during the evening, with hefty fines for anyone found under the influence at work. The groups are all united in demanding drug-testing for bosses. Naturally, this doesn't sit well with executives who like a quickie during their coffee break. They could never fit it in before because they couldn't get it up. With the miracle of Niagra, now they can!

HMOs are reluctant to pay for the new drug, unless the man has demonstrated a pre-existing problem with impotence. "Lots of men think Niagra is a free ticket to fool around," their spokesman declared, "but we have to make a sound judgment about medical necessity. The purpose of this drug is not to have a good time. There has to be a verifiable attempt at procreation here, or we can't pay for it. There is no clear advantage to engaging in sexual relations more than once a month. Anyone who has sex more often than that is just having fun, and we won't have it."

Another unexpected side-effect is seeing everything with a bluish tinge. This, along with the aforementioned dizziness, has led to frequent reports of alien abductions. Paralyzed with nocturnal erections, these unfortunate men levitate toward flying saucers hovering outside their bedroom windows. Inside the spaceship, they are probed and examined by bluish-looking beings with buggy eyes. These little blue men extract sperm samples from their subjects' accommodating members, and once they've got them in this vulnerable position, they have their way with them as well.

Animal Shelter Opens Doors to Homeless

San Francisco: The local animal shelter has announced that it's opening its doors to the homeless. "With all the inclement weather we've been having, we'd like to do our part in helping people get off the street," a spokesperson said.

Some animal rights activists have protested this decision to house the homeless, claiming the over-crowding will eliminate precious space for many deserving animals, the "innocent victims" of the housing crisis that faces this city. But the shelter contends that adding humans to the population in no way reduces their capacity to take in abandoned pets, since they wouldn't normally put more than one dog or cat in a cage, anyway. "Humans get along pretty well with most cats and dogs," the spokesperson explained. "So we like to put them together to keep each other company." He defended the new policy by saying, "After all, people are animals, too."

Edgar Jenks, a homeless man, is happy as a hound dog in his new digs. "I get to park my shopping cart in the back, out of the rain, and bring in whatever comforts I want to make my cage real homey." Edgar has a new roomie—a cuddly pit bull named Spike, who's kept separate from the other dogs because of his tendency to nip off their heels.

"Before Spike, I bunked with Butch, the friendliest English bull dog you ever did see, only he kept me awake all night licking my face!"

The cages are all reinforced iron, with just enough room for an adult dog to turn around. Edgar often huddles in the corner playing his ukulele, while Spike gambols about, chases his tail, or nibbles at Edgar's ears. Each occupant has his own stainless steel drinking bowl, and twice a day he gets his choice of wet or dry dog food. "Spike likes the liver-flavored wet, but I actually prefer the dry," Edgar said. "I like the crunch."

During the day, Edgar gets to exercise in the dog-run, and can often be seen frolicking and cavorting with the other dogs (only Spike has to stay inside, because of his tendency to get into gang fights). During nice weather, Edgar takes Spike out on a leash and visits some of his old haunts—the dumpsters on Sixth Street, the steam vents alongside the Department of Public Health, and Saint Anthony's food line. "I kinda miss the camaraderie of the old soup kitchen," Edgar admitted, "but you can't beat my crunchy kibbles for a filling meal!"

Nor does he miss the flophouse where he used to land whenever he saved enough dough from panhandling. "You'd have your drug addicts running up and down the hall, high as a kite, looking for their next fix; your crazies jabbering about the heebie jeebies gonna get 'em; your religious fanatics wailing and gnashing their teeth—it was a regular bedlam. Whereas the dog pound is a welcome harbor in a storm, where I can snuggle up with Spike and while away the night. The mutts and mongrels howling at the moon in their soulful chorus is music to my ears, compared to the goings on in that fleabite hotel."

Every couple of days, Edgar and Spike get a nice dusting to keep off the ticks and fleas, which is more than the homeless shelter in the Tenderloin ever provided.

On Sundays, the animal shelter sets up a few cages in the midst of a neighborhood shopping district, like Fillmore Street in Pacific Heights, where potential adopters can *ooh* and *aah* at the adorable kitties and pooches, and youngsters get their fingers nipped through the bars. One sunny weekend, they brought Edgar along with Spike in an extra-large cage. "This is part of our outreach to the community," the spokesperson explained. "We like to encourage co-adoptions, so we can avoid separating the siblings in a litter. Since Spike and Edgar get along so well, we were kinda hoping to keep them together, in case anyone's interested. Of course, if only one of them gets an offer, we won't hold him back."

Curious passers-by seemed puzzled at seeing a grown man in the cage with Spike. "Is he house-broken?" they'd ask. "Does he do windows?" Edgar played his ukulele, while Spike bit the fingers off a couple of children.

Sadly, at the end of the day, there were no takers. Nevertheless, Edgar and Spike were glad they could still be together, and they looked forward to the comfort of their own cage back at the pound.

Kansas Board of Education Decrees: Earth Is Flat

WICHITA: The Kansas State Board of Education announced its decision today to require the state's geography teachers to disregard Magellan, and teach students that the earth is flat.

Julian Bock, President of the Board, said "We're tired of so-called scientists defying common sense by insisting that the earth is round. The next thing you know they'll start claiming the earth goes around the sun! When all you have to do is look out the window to see that the sun comes up; then it goes down. Duh!"

Geography teachers were stunned. A group of them got together to present a petition to the board, calling for a reconsideration of their decision. Susan Brownsmith, a spokesperson for the group, said "This requirement makes Kansas look like it's stuck in the fourteenth century. There is no way that we will teach such an absurd statement as scientific fact."

Mr. Bock responded to her criticism by suggesting that those teachers who were still baffled by this policy, must at the very least explain to their students that the earth being round is only a theory, which has never been proven; after all, who was around when the earth was created?

"Many of the puzzles that abound in nature can just as readily be explained by another scientific theory—namely, that the earth is flat. I can think of any number of natural phenomena that can be adequately explained by flat-earth science," Mr. Bock claimed.

When asked to name one, he scratched his head for a moment, looking a bit consternated. Then he brightened up, and said "Isn't it clear that there would be no people south of the equator if the earth was round? They would all fall off!" he grinned at his own brilliance. "I think gravity is one of the most cogent proofs of flat-earth science. They can't very well argue with gravity, can they? I dare say even in New Zealand, kiwis still fall to the ground. These petitioners are absurdly stubborn in their refusal to look at the truth, which is unambiguous and indisputable. All you have to do is open your eyes!"

In their petition, the geography teachers outlined a number of counters to this so-called theory. "Look at the moon during the lunar eclipse" was one of their suggestions.

Mr. Bock slapped the petition with the back of his hand. "As if that proved anything," he scoffed. "Just because you see a roundish shadow on the moon doesn't mean the earth is round like a ball—it only shows that the earth is round like a pancake! Isn't that simple?

"Here's another so-called proof. 'A round earth explains how a ship's mast is the last thing you see as it slips over the horizon.' Naturally a ship's going to disappear as it approaches the horizon. Things get smaller as they move further away. The ship gets so small that eventually you can't even see it. Because it has shrunk to such a teensy weensy size, it appears that the only part left is the mast. Every scientist knows that appearances can be deceiving. You have to use your common sense!

"And despite the distortions of our position reported by the biased news media, we are definitely not disregarding Magellan. A ship sailing around the world is of course going to come back where it started, just like a phonograph record goes 'round and 'round. And those photos from space! Another blue pancake! Who are they trying to fool?"

Finally, Mr. Bock said, "You know, there are democratic principles at stake here. Most people think it's only fair to give both sides of a dispute. That's fine; we can be open-minded. Go ahead and teach flat-earth science versus the discredited notion of a spherical world. Let the students decide for themselves."

Ms. Brownsmith objected that science was not a democratic process, but a method for developing an increasingly accurate picture of the natural world. "Students shouldn't be told that whether or not the earth is flat is merely a matter of opinion," she said. "Despite the ignorant claims of the majority, the truth should not be subjected to a popular vote."

Mr. Bock shook his head. "I'm sorry there's such a lack of respect for the democratic process among the teachers of our state. We voted on this, and the teachers must follow the mandate of the Board."

Since then, all the teachers who refused to teach flat-earth science have been fired.

The Dog in the Freezer

I WAS A SOPHOMORE in high school during my brother Jeff's first year in college, when he demonstrated his aptitude for zoology by reconstructing the skeletons of rodents he had trapped in the foothills above our home.

The remains of rats being quite small and delicate, their skeletons kept collapsing in a heap of bones. Ecological scruples and a kind heart prevented him from trapping any larger game, but his dilemma was potentially resolved through the donation by a local veterinarian of a small dog that had perished from natural causes, and been frozen, awaiting just such an opportunity to beat back the frontiers of science.

Jeff hopped on his bike Saturday morning and rode over to the vet's to pick up the dog. Since he was in the midst of midterms, he didn't have time to tackle his latest specimen right away; so he stashed its carcass in the ice cream compartment of our freezer while Mom was out shopping, then promptly threw himself into his studies. Dad was watching a football game on TV, and I was in my room, reading; so neither of us knew he'd even left the house.

When Mom came home and put away the groceries, she was startled to find the remains of someone's recently departed pet when she tried to insert a Sara Lee carrot cake into the frozen dessert section. "Yikes!" she said.

Dad, who was absorbed in the gladiatorial rout of USC by Purdue, looked up and said "Hmm?"

Mom rushed into the den. "There's a dog in our freezer."

Dad gave her a laconic stare, as our mother tended toward alarmist pronouncements, though she had mustered a strained calm that lent a certain credibility to her statement.

However, it being the third down in the last two minutes of the fourth quarter, Dad was not in the mood to deal with dogs in the freezer, so he turned back to his game, figuring she meant "clog" instead of "dog," and he'd check on it later.

Mom proceeded down the hall to my room, where she found me engrossed in Mead's *Coming of Age in Samoa*. "Can you explain why there's a dog in the freezer?" she asked.

Supposing this was a riddle, I bit my thumbnail and stared at the ceiling. "Why was the dog in the freezer? Because, uh . . . because . . ."

Mom tapped her foot impatiently. "Well?" she demanded.

I said "I'm *thinking*." She rolled her eyes at me, about to say something, but I held up my hand. "Don't tell me—um . . . I know, it was so hot, the dog snuck into the freezer to lick the ice, and his tongue stuck to the tray." I looked up in anticipation, but she shook her head, and threw her hands in the air. Without telling me the answer, she marched down the hall to ask Jeff the same riddle. I followed her to his room and peered over her shoulder.

Jeff was putting the finishing touches on the rat skeleton he had glued to a piece of cardboard. He kept trying to get it to stand up, like the skeletons of dinosaurs they have in museums. Calculus books and term papers on *The Brothers Karamazov* and post-Jeffersonian democracy lay strewn about his desk and across the floor.

He wiped his finger on his jeans to get the glue off, because whenever he pushed one of the tiny bones down to the cardboard it pulled back up again. "It's for zoology," he said, which I found an even less likely solution than the one I'd bumbled across.

"I am not concerned," my mother said, "with its biological classification. I would like to know what it's doing in the freezer!"

"Waiting," said Jeff, and flicked his finger, the tiny bone now stuck to his skin.

"Waiting!" Mom exclaimed.

"I'm in the middle of midterms!" Jeff said, fairly exasperated, batting his finger against his thumb trying to shake the bone off, while he held down the hind leg of the skeleton with a pair of tweezers.

"I know you are, honey," she said, speaking with the voice one assumes with those who are addled, "I just wonder if you would explain what the little dog is waiting for, and while you're at it, why it's waiting for whatever it's waiting for in *my freezer*?"

Jeff finally glanced up from his project, and said "The dog, I think, has a better chance of standing up."

He looked down at the rat, which was now quite flat against the cardboard.

I said "Come on, Mom, give us a hint."

She developed a frantic look in her eyes, and retreated to the kitchen, tiptoed around the refrigerator, and grabbed her phone book. She rapidly dialed Dr. Shoemaker at home. "There's a dog in our freezer!" she said.

There must have been a subdued silence on the other end, because she tapped the hook-switch and said "Hello? Hello?" She finally understood the doctor was out, and clarified for Mrs. Shoemaker her concern that the dog might be a deadly source of ptomaine, typhus, or worse, and wanted to know if it had contaminated our food.

After a number of probings, answered by a short "Yes," "No," and "I think so," the doctor's wife tried to reassure my mother that since the animal had been transported home without defrosting and was carefully wrapped in plastic, it should pose no more of a threat to the contents of our freezer than a package of frozen hot dogs.

Nonetheless, Mom unloaded all the frozen desserts from the compartment with the dog, and stuffed them into other sections of the freezer. She asked if I would like the last dab from a carton of rocky road ice cream that wouldn't quite fit elsewhere.

"Not particularly," I said. I headed back to my room, still trying to figure out what the answer would have been if there really was such a riddle. As I passed his doorway, Jeff wanted to know if Mom had asked the doc whether he thought a dog skeleton was more likely to stand up. I shrugged, and continued down the hall, suggesting he could pursue the point with her at his peril.

When I reached my bedroom, suddenly it came to me. I snapped my fingers and rushed back to the kitchen, where Mom still knelt by the freezer, scowling at the frozen dog. "Mom! I've got it: his master said 'Fetch me the Cold Duck'!" She looked at me with an uncomprehending gaze. I ran to my brother's room, laughing like a maniac. "Jeff! Fetch me the Cold Duck!" I yelled, and slapped him on the back.

"Get out of here!" he said, not in the mood.

I scampered down the hall to my room, and shut the door. Feeling smug, I flopped on my bed and re-immersed myself in the slightly less puzzling riddle of South Pacific adolescence.

Clinton Fesses Up to Fooling Around

My fellow Americans, this is a difficult time for me, and I know it's been a difficult time for you. There have been allegations of lies, cover-ups, and undue influence in the matter regarding Ms. Lewinsky, so I thought it was time to set the record straight.

While we never had sexual intercourse, and I believe I was telling the truth when I denied under oath that we ever had sex, I do admit that Monica sucked my dick. I understand that oral sex would be construed by most people as a violation of my marriage vows, which I freely acknowledge.

You know, I've always been a ladies' man, and that's gotten me into trouble more than once. After Gennifer Flowers, to say nothing of Paula Jones, you'd think I would have learned my lesson, but the trappings of power tend to propel my recklessness to new heights. I have to say, having Monica suck me off in the Oval Office while talking on the phone to members of Congress really got my rocks off.

There's something about the danger of getting caught that thrills me and goads me to increasingly irresponsible sexual antics. Flaunting my power and sexual magnetism totally turns me on. You'd think with everything at stake in Iraq, Bosnia, and the Middle East that I would control my predilection for self-indulgence, but if anything that level of responsibility actually fuels my lascivious passions.

At the same time, while admitting the rashness of my own actions, it's also true that the right wing in this country would do anything to discredit me—not that they have to try very hard, but their hypocritical and moralistic vendetta has definitely backfired on them. I frankly suspect most guys get a kick out of a good blow-job, and even a lot of women can identify with

Monica's fawning admiration for a certain symbol of power. Oh, that rascally Bill! And he got away with it! Good for him.

I'm proud of our fight against impeachment, which I believe saved the Constitution (along with my own sorry ass) from a vast, right-wing conspiracy. Still, that's not to say I don't have a problem. But it's the kind of human frailty that many folks can identify with, and I suppose that's what I'm counting on with the American people.

So, I'm sorry I misrepresented the truth about these matters. I know I've disappointed a lot of people—my wife, my daughter, and the leaders of my own party—but I've also disappointed you, the American people, for not living up to the ideals of leadership and responsibility you've come to expect from your President.

I admit that I fucked up. All I can count on is the good will and basic decency of fair-minded folks such as yourselves. I have some glaring, but ultimately human flaws, and I can only hope y'all will forgive me. Let's join together and put this unhappy episode behind us.

Queen for a Day

OUR NEXT contestant is Samantha Alighieri, known affectionately by her friends as "Sam the Man," who recently arrived here from Kickapoo, Oklahoma. Let's hear it for Sam the Man!

~

Howdy! When I started working out, my girlfriends teased me. "You getting to be some butch dyke, girl!" Can you believe I used to be skinny? No more Miss Prissy Pants, here. I will seriously deck anyone who gets in my way, so don't fuck with me.

Who's out there, anyway? I can't hardly see for all these stage lamps glaring in my face. I recognize some of you. What's a P.C. dyke like you, doing in a place like this?

What is this, "Queen for a Day"—pitting woman against woman, for the pleasure of The Man? It's patriarchal, hierarchical, capitalist class oppression! I am a socialist feminist, anarcho-syndicalist, woman-identified Woman! But desperate times call for desperate measures. If you happen to like my story, go ahead and clap—Real Loud. And if you enjoy the other ladies' stories, you can clap politely for them, too.

I came to these parts with my girlfriend Jolene. We first met when I mended her fence last summer. The morning I started working on the barbed wire, Jolene appeared on the horizon, picking wildflowers. She gathered them in her apron and made a daisy chain for her hair. I felt my heart swell, but she took no notice of me. I sighed, and just kept twisting those barbs, trying to forget about her. What's the use of coming on to a farmer's wife? But when I looked up again, she was hustling those thighs like a heifer in heat, thundering toward me from clear across the pasture!

She said at first her husband mistook me for a man, and was getting kinda worked up about it, but then he relaxed about our friendship once she clarified my true gender. He was glad she'd found some female companionship so she'd stop driving him batty with all her chit-chat. But I didn't mind it at all. After a long spell of loneliness, I found her sweet nothings quite pleasurable. Once I finished working on their fence, she started coming over to my place. Every afternoon, while her husband was out working the fields, we'd smooch in the shade of the haystack, me in my overalls, Jolene in her party dress, and watch the heat waves rising off the prairie.

One evening, her husband came looking for her and caught us spooning in the moonlight. He aimed his shotgun and blew the top off the haystack, but Jolene and I escaped into town and caught a bus all the way to San Francisco!

We didn't much care for city life, so we started a sprout farm and tofu factory up on the Russian River. Our chickens laid only unfertilized eggs—we wouldn't allow no cock-a-doodle-do in our chicken coop!

This was my ultimate dream come true. We were so in love! I skimmed the scum off the tofu while Jolene gathered eggs and watered the sprouts, then we'd snuggle together under our tin roof when it started to rain. Only it kept raining, for days on end, never letting up until the river began to swell. We woke up one morning to find the current lapping at the steps of our tofu factory!

Jolene rushed out to check the chickens, while I closed up the vats—but the water kept rising! When I came outside, the river swirled through the yard, and Jolene crawled on top of the chicken coop. "Sam!" she cried. The coop lurched to one side.

I shouted "Hold on, Jolene!" and waded toward her. But the water rose faster and faster, and before I could reach her, the coop swept right into the river!

Jolene hung on tight, her chickens flapping their wings and squawking in a panic—*brawr, ba ba bawr*! I dove into the boiling rapids, while Jolene bobbed ahead of me, bellowing "Save me, Sam! *Save* me!

I churned my arms, swallowing buckets of river water, the rain splattered across my face as I kicked through the debris, hollering "Hold on, Jolene! Hold on!" and chased that coop all the way to Jenner.

The coop skipped over the waves, got caught by a current and swept clear out to sea. I did my best to battle the tide, throwing myself against wave after wave, until a huge breaker picked me up and crushed me on the shore. "Sam!" cried Jolene from across the water, "I—love—*you*!" She waved a last, lonely good-bye as she drifted over the horizon.

Last sighted off the coast of Ecuador, she was floating south on top of that chicken coop. I don't mind losing the tofu factory, or the sprout farm, or even the chickens. Hell, I've started over before, and I'll do it again. But I lost the *only* woman I ever loved. If you make me *Queen for a Day*, I won't rest till I find my Jolene, even if I have to sail all the way to Tierra del Fuego!

Point-Counterpoint:

Margaret Thatcher vs. Oscar Wilde

GOOD EVENING, ladies and gentlemen, and welcome to the World Leadership Symposium. Our scheduled debate features Baroness Margaret Thatcher, the "Iron Lady" and former Prime Minister of the United Kingdom, who squares off tonight with Mr. Oscar Wilde, playwright, wag, and man about town. We look forward to a lively exchange of views, and a most enlightening evening.

LADY THATCHER: I was not always popular. Reformers rarely are while their reforms are going through, though if we struggle on we reap the rewards later.

MR. WILDE: It is a dangerous thing to reform anyone. I don't desire to change anything in England except the weather.

LADY THATCHER: One only gets to the top rung on the ladder by steadily climbing up one at a time, and suddenly, all sorts of powers, all sorts of abilities which you thought never belonged to you—suddenly become within your own possibility and you think, "Well, I'll have a go, too."

MR. WILDE: Real industry becomes simply the refuge of people who have nothing whatever to do.

~

Lady Thatcher: Look at a day when you are supremely satisfied at the end. It's not a day when you lounge around doing nothing; it's when you've had everything to do, and you've done it.

Mr. Wilde: Cultivated leisure is the aim of man.

~

Lady Thatcher: I believe politicians must see that religious education has a proper place in the school curriculum.

Mr. Wilde: I never came across anyone in whom the moral sense was dominant who was not heartless, cruel, vindictive, log-stupid, and entirely lacking in the smallest sense of humanity. I like persons better than principles, and I like persons with no principles better than anything else in the world.

~

Lady Thatcher: Platitudes? Yes, there are platitudes. Platitudes are there because they are true.

Mr. Wilde: The truth is rarely pure and never simple.

~

Lady Thatcher: Of course it's the same old story. Truth usually is the same old story.

Mr. Wilde: The things one feels absolutely certain about are never true. That is the fatality of Faith, and the lesson of Romance.

~

LADY THATCHER: You don't tell deliberate lies, but sometimes you have to be evasive.

MR. WILDE: It is a terrible thing for a man to find out suddenly that all his life he has been speaking nothing but the truth. If one tells the truth, one is sure, sooner or later, to be found out.

LADY THATCHER: We know now that it is free enterprise capitalism that works best to foster innovation and create jobs.

MR. WILDE: There is something tragic about the enormous number of young men there are in England at the present moment who start life with perfect profiles, and end by adopting some useful profession.

LADY THATCHER: It is not the creation of wealth that is wrong, but the love of money for its own sake. Any set of social and economic arrangements which is not founded on the acceptance of individual responsibility will do nothing but harm.

MR. WILDE: It is immoral to use private property in order to alleviate the horrible evils that result from the institution of private property.

Lady Thatcher: Standing in the middle of the road is very dangerous; you get knocked down by the traffic from both sides.

Mr. Wilde: One should never take sides in anything. Taking sides is the beginning of sincerity and earnestness follows shortly afterward, and the human being becomes a bore.

Lady Thatcher: Pennies do not come from heaven—they have to be earned here on earth.

Mr. Wilde: The rich harp on the value of thrift, the idle grow eloquent over the dignity of labor.

Lady Thatcher: Success is having a flair for the thing that you are doing; knowing that it is not enough, that you have got to have hard work and a certain sense of purpose.

Mr. Wilde: We live in the age of the overworked, and the undereducated; the age in which people are so industrious that they become absolutely stupid.

Lady Thatcher: It's passionately interesting for me that the things that I learned in a small town, in a very modest home, are just the things that I believe have won the election.

Mr. Wilde: Anybody can be good in the country. There are no temptations there. They get up early because they have so much to do and go to bed early because they have so little to think about.

Lady Thatcher: The world is the kind of place in which conservatives are still needed.

Mr. Wilde: The prig is a very interesting psychological study, and though of all poses a moral pose is the most offensive, still to have a pose at all is something.

Lady Thatcher: I am in politics because of the struggle between good and evil. I believe that in the end good will triumph.

Mr. Wilde: When we are happy we are always good, but when we are good we are not always happy.

Heaven Talks Back

NOWADAYS every Jack and his brother is having a Near Death Experience. At the end of a long tunnel bathed in white light, you meet Aunt Sally or Uncle Joe, fit as a gipper, welcoming you home—only the time ain't right—you gotta go back and tell folks there ain't nothing to worry about, 'cause death is one big Picnic in the Sky. Now everybody wants to get into the act, so I figure it's time to give some instruction on how to work an audience.

You play a big auditorium and say, I hear the voice of a woman named Mary. Someone in the audience is bound to gasp, "That's my mother/daughter/sister!" Was it an accident? (no) A serious illness? (emphatic nod) Cancer? (Yes!) Well don't you worry your little honey buns, 'cause your sis is doing just fine in the Great Beyond. (Cock your head) What's that, Mary? There was some misunderstanding betwixt the two of you, and you never came to terms with it before you died? (woman sobs) Well, dear sister, rest assured. Mary forgives you with all her heart and wishes you and her husband all the happiness in the world (she collapses in the arms of the man next to her).

What's that, you say? I'm just reading off the cues people give me? Well you're a galdarned spoiler with your conniving skepticism. No, I wasn't talking to Mary's sister out in the hall. Mister, you are seriously messing with other people's minds! 'Course I can't talk to your mother, 'cause your heart is closed, the energy's all tight and clamped down. The Spirits only come in when they're invited, they ain't some kinda interloping gate-crasher like yourself.

Now take this good family over here. A proud, bereaved father in his mature years, an obviously grieving mother. Was it your son? (nodding) A terrible accident? (no) A long and lingering illness, like AIDS? (no) A murder? (no) (slow down, now close your eyes and place palm on your forehead). Oh my God in creation—it wasn't—(look them straight in the eye)—Suicide? (nods, tears, the mother covers her face) Gunshot? (shake their heads) Pills? (no) Slicer dicer? (nodding) He cut his wrists! You found him yourselves, I bet, in the laundry hamper. Oh, what an awful calamity. But what's this? (raise both hands and close your eyes) I see him, I see him right there, standing behind you, beaming a smile big enough to beat the band! (look at them now) He says it wasn't your fault—you both did the best you could, even though you never really understood him. He's just glad to be released from this vale of tears.

I see a poor, innocent little child, hardly more than a babe. (a moan rises from the crowd) Was it yours? (point out the woman) Crib death? (no) Birth defect? (no) Uh, left out in the rain? Run over by a train? Skipped town? (get hold of yourself, now, you're grasping at straws) Abducted by aliens? (gulp, nod, more tears, her husband holding her up) Well rest assured, your little baby is safe with Jesus, I see him cradled in His arms, smilin' and cooing, gazing down on you with all the love you wish you could have given him. (tears streaming) Just be grateful for the short, sweet time you had together, for no one knows the time or place we'll be called home to Jesus. (uncontrollable sobbing) Don't worry, you'll have another baby.

So, Mr. Know-it-All, ain't that proof enough? No? I suspected as much, Mr. Smarty-Pants. Have you no decency, no respect—if not for the dead, at least for the bereft and grieving? (gesture toward the couple, palm up) How dare you scoff so cynically at this broken-hearted family of a dearly departed child?

Does the name Duffy, Buffy, Huffy, Ruffy, Tuffy, or Muffy mean anything to anyone? ("Muffy! That was my sweet dog! She died over forty years ago!") Well your little puppy is still scampering around, barking up trees, chasing down squirrels, and chewing up socks in the sky! Wait—what's that, Muffy? I know you're excited, but you gotta slow down the vibrations so I can catch what you're saying. Oh! here it comes—

"Dr. Ross dogfood is dog-gone good—Woof!"

Left-Handed Alliance Opposed by Religious Right

ORANGE, CALIFORNIA: The Religious Right announced its opposition to the formation of a new alliance between left- and right-handed students at Leeward High School. Harlan Dexter, a spokesman for a group of parents, spoke at a news conference today. "This is obviously a sinister plot to normalize left-handedness, and introduce leftist propaganda into the schools."

Jeffrey Levoro, 16, a left-handed student, disagreed. "This is just a club for lefties to get together and share some of our concerns. We'd like to have fun and socialize in an atmosphere free of intimidation. We welcome right-handed students to join us, so they can learn that we're really not that different. That might help change the attitudes of those students who have an irrational fear of left-handedness. We call it 'portaphobia.' "

"Left-handedness is not a true minority, it's just gauche behavior," Mr. Dexter claimed. "No one is born left-handed, and even if a child has maladroit tendencies, we certainly don't want to encourage it by suggesting being left-handed is normal. Think of all the impressionable young people who might experiment with left-handedness once it's actually sponsored by the schools!"

"We're not claiming that left is better, and we're not trying to get anybody else to try it," Jeffrey said. "We're just saying left-handedness is a normal variation in humans, and there's nothing wrong with it. We should be able to use our left hand as our dominant hand without being harassed, threatened, or discriminated against."

"Left is not right!" Mr. Dexter exclaimed. "We shouldn't be fostering the idea that left is okay, when right is clearly better. And we shouldn't lend any legitimacy to the leftist lifestyle. It's time for tough-love here, not some freewheeling, indulgent twaddle. All students should be required to use their right hand."

"Numerous studies have documented the damage that's done to children when you force them to use their right hand," Jeffrey said. "Left-handed kids are commonly hit, their left hands are tied behind their backs, they're humiliated and shunned as 'goofy-footed southpaws.'"

"You can't tell me that left-handed people can't become right-handed," Mr. Dexter countered. "If they really put their minds to it, it's possible. We have plenty of formerly left-handed members of our own church who can write, eat, and throw a ball with their right hand. They struggled with their affliction, but with the help of prayer, practice, and diligence, they finally got it right. It's leftist propaganda that left-handers can't change."

"Sure, some left-handers are able to pass as right-handed," Jeffrey acknowledged. "But just because a few left-handed people can become ambidextrous doesn't mean that they're not really left-handed. They're just pretending, so they can avoid persecution. If you ask them if they ever fantasize about using their left hand, most will admit they do. Many so-called 'ex-lefties' even confess that in the privacy of their own homes, they still eat, write, and throw baseballs with their left hand."

"This has no business being brought up at school," another parent objected. "I don't want my kids subjected to propaganda suggesting that it's all right to be left-handed, undermining the moral values I'm teaching at home. Ecclesiastes tells us, '*A wise man's heart inclines him toward the right, but a fool's heart toward the left.*'"

Jeffrey said, "We've come up with a list of famous left-handed people in history, to show that left-handedness is not necessarily a handicap, or any indication of laziness or moral turpitude: Alexander the Great, Joan of Arc, Leonardo da Vinci, Michelangelo, James Baldwin, and Rock Hudson. This gives young lefties a certain amount of pride to realize we're not alone, there's nothing wrong with it, and there's no reason to change."

Mr. Dexter challenged this assertion. "They claim they're just concerned about right-handed bullies, when this is really part of a larger conspiracy to legitimize the left-handed lifestyle," he said. "We're all for protecting children, but their agenda is to get this into the curriculum.

"We don't want our kids confused by thinking that being left-handed is a decent or acceptable choice. Once they allow a Left-Right Alliance, it will open the door to all kinds of school-sponsored activities advocating the leftist lifestyle—Left-handed Pride Day, left-handed dancing, left-handed scissors—what's next? Driving on the left side of the road? It's un-American!"

Jeffrey said, "Again, we're not trying to recruit other kids to become left-handed; we're just tired of everyone telling us we should be right-handed, because we're not. We're born this way, it's perfectly natural, it's just that there's fewer of us, that's all. If we were the majority, you'd be saying the same thing about right-handed people."

"That's utter nonsense. A child should be taught that right is right, and left is wrong," Mr. Dexter said. "Why befuddle innocent youths with the notion that left is right, when it's so obviously not? How are they supposed to know which way to turn?"

Meanwhile, the school board is considering the option of banning all campus groups, just to avoid any more controversy.

Coupe de Ville

My first mistake was my soft spot for a cushy set of wheels. Al, my bud from Skokie, says I attract attention snoozing in a cruisemobile. But if you got a choice between a tin can and a divan, I say take the divan. It gets you out of the rain, and you don't bang your knees against the front seat every time you turn over.

So I been crashing nearly every night for the last couple of weeks in this '69 Coupe de Ville near 15th and Mission, in Frisco. No tires, steel on the asphalt, but still a little spring in the suspension. Days, I leave my acquisitions in the coupe. You walk around with a blanket or a bundle, you look down and out. Al says, "Lou, you got an image problem."

I punch a crease in my felt crusher and tip it back on my head. "What image? I just don't want to look like some bum."

"But chyar, Blanche, y'are a bum." Al's such a card.

I'm not normally what you'd call a tough palooka. Some joker's got a bone to pick, I take a powder. I seen too many busted jaws and gimp shoulders to scrap with winos on the street. But I am partial to the back seat of my Cad—it would take a lot to budge me. So when I wake up one drizzly morning with this jughead passed out in the front seat, I get properly on his case. "Hey, you," I say, "this bench is taken." I get no response, so I swat his butt. "You, buddy, I'm talking to you! Take a walk." Not a stir. This time I reach down and yank him by the collar. "Hey, pisspot!" His head rolls back, his hat falls off, and I see the sucker got his throat slit, his eyes still bugging at the dim gray dawn.

My first thought, there goes the neighborhood. I can't have no corpse living next door. I seen enough wormbait, though, not to get nauseated. These jokers down in the Tenderloin find some stiff and lean him up against the wall. When you brush by him he falls right on you or crashes his skull on the concrete. A prime example of a truly perverse sense of humor.

I wasn't scared, though it could've just as easily been me. Except his clothes looked a lot nicer than mine: linen trousers, silk shirt, Armani blazer. You got what other people want, they get jealous. You get a little, you want more—it's the American way. I ain't knocking it; just never panned out for me.

That's why Al warns me about putting on airs, with my highfalootin taste in accommodations. Though he has his own image problem. He can't stand the "homeless," says they're crowding our territory, jamming the food lines, giving panhandlers a bad name. Claims he used to ride the rails in the old days, so he somehow rates? It's like the old immigrants always resent the new ones. When it comes down to it, I figure we're all off the same boat.

Normally an honest person, I never understood the problem with fleecing a corpse. They got no use for nothing left in this world. The damage already done, I check to see if he's got any loot. Wallet gone, no watch. Stick 'em and slice 'em job. I'm not about to rip off his bloody threads—you got to draw the line somewhere.

My second mistake was not going to the cops, though it couldn't have done this bastard no good. Who would believe some tramp off the street, anyway? Going through his rags, I start to get jumpy. Not wanting to get caught rifling a dead man's pockets, I grab my bundle and fly the coop. But no sooner I get five blocks away, I realize I left behind my hat. You'd think to keep from getting popped I'd ditch the old felt sombrero, but it's my lucky hat. Been with me more places, gotten me out of more jams than I can shake my whoopee at. I had to go back.

I'm nosin' in the back seat, my tail swaying in the breeze, when this flatfoot pulls me out by my beltloop. He slams me spread-eagled across the trunk and shoves his club against my throat. "Whatcha lookin' for, 'bo?"

In court, I told the gavel jockey it wasn't my car. This, though technically correct, was my third mistake. I had in a manner of speaking secured squatter's rights, and should have explained I was casing the coupe to find my hat. The dick that pinched me claimed he found blood stains on my duds. But I denied ever laying eyes on the Cad before and never saw the body, then 'cause I acted so jacked up of course Father Time gives me a free pass to the Crossbar Hotel—Murder One.

No sense trying to call no one for bail—nobody's home. After a few weeks, though, Al gets picked up and joins me in the slammer. "Hey, Lou," he says, "heard through the vine you been stowed in the hoosegow. How long you in for?" He only gets a night or two at best before they chuck him out in the cold.

"I'm going down for some time to come, Al. The public defender guarantees it."

Ten Commandments Posted at Post Office

BRONX: Following another incident of a disgruntled post office worker going "postal," the postmaster of the local post office decided to post the Ten Commandments to prevent any further mayhem. "If it's good enough for Moses, I guess it's good enough for the Bronx," the postmaster said.

Postal workers interviewed about this development all agreed that it was a good idea. Fred Ferrari, a counter clerk, said "You got your lunatic fringe in any business, but sometimes you just gotta take a break and consider the consequences of your actions. With the Ten Commandments right there in front of your nose, you're gonna think twice before you bring a semi-automatic to work and blow away your fellow workers. Or at least pause before you clap on another clip. I think it could save a lotta lives."

A district court judge objected to the intrusion of religious icons into the public sphere. "Of course it's not good for morale to kill employees, but you don't want to look like you're endorsing any particular religion," the judge explained. He ordered the postmaster to take down the engraved tablets. "It's okay to establish reasonable workplace standards, but let's not call them the Ten Commandments. There's just too many religious connotations."

Religious leaders condemned the intrusion of the state into what they regard as a purely private expression of religious sentiment. "You're curbing the legitimate expression of free speech by the postmaster," they argued.

Nevertheless, the postmaster went along with the judge's ruling. "You gotta obey the law, that's the whole point," he said. "Anyway, a lot of that stuff in there doesn't really apply that well to the workplace. I mean, we gotta stay open on Saturday—that's the only day a lotta people get off work. And graven images?

Like stamps? What's so bad about that? And what's not to covet? They're collector's items."

So he put up a new sign, which expressed some similar ideas, but in a different style of speaking:

Ten New Workplace Standards

1. Please don't bring guns to work. Even if you like keeping your weapon handy, it can lead to impulsive behavior you may regret later.
2. If you're pissed off, file a grievance, don't fire your weapon.
3. If a customer gives you a hard time, just tell them to bug off. You don't have to shoot them.
4. Even if you're having a really bad day, please don't kill your fellow employees. They're just doing their job, and everybody's got to get by one way or the other.
5. Don't covet your coworker's ass. If you like her, that's fine, but don't just put a move on her—try asking her out.
6. If you ask someone for a date and she turns you down, that's a bummer. But it's no reason to go off half-cocked and shoot someone, and it's not cool to force yourself on her either.
7. If you've been sexually harassed, come and talk to me about it so we can confront the offender and work something out, rather than shooting him.
8. If you make a mistake, well, just try to do better next time. If you really can't cut it, maybe you should find another job, because you're not going to get a very good reference after you've blown everybody away.
9. What else? Oh yeah, don't lie, cheat, steal, or otherwise act like a wise guy at work.
10. And another thing. Try smiling at your customers. A little friendliness never killed anyone.

You Can Be Gay!

VISTA, CALIFORNIA: The Christian Conglomerate is having a field day over the exposure of a gay recruitment flyer discovered yesterday circulating around Greenfield High School. "This is exactly what we've been fussing about!" their spokesman said in an interview this morning. "Liberals scoff when we claim homosexuals try to recruit unsuspecting youngsters to their venal, lascivious lifestyle, but now we have proof!"

After the flyer's bold headline, *YOU CAN BE GAY!*, there follows a list of ten enticements to enter the gay lifestyle:

1. Nowadays, it's cool to be gay. Homophobes are totally retro.
2. You'll always get the quickest access to the latest fashions, hairstyles, and music.
3. You'll become instantly more creative, artistic, and in-the-know.
4. You're friends will think you're awesome!
5. Your parents will croak!
6. No more football games!
7. You don't have to get married!
8. It's the best way to get out of the Boy Scouts! (Have you seen their uniforms? Gag me.)
9. Forget the military! March to a different drummer!
10. You can do it! Be the first kid on your block to turn gay!

The flyer offers the number for the nearest gay youth recruitment center. "The first twenty kids to sign up this week get a Barbra Streissand CD, a video of *The Wizard of Oz*, and a rainbow flag!"

The Christian Conglomerate spokesman warned, "We are in dire danger of our youth being corrupted by the homosexual lifestyle. Beware of vile, seditious influences! Here are some ominous signs to watch out for: stylish haircuts and fashionable clothes; an excessive interest in classical music, dance, art, or poetry; expressing disdain for regimented sports; whistling show tunes; developing a taste in foreign cuisine; speaking French; or redecorating the living room.

"Another tell-tale sign is the avoidance of heterosexual dating by joining the debate team or the marching band; becoming a thespian; or by forming close friendships with students of the opposite sex.

"The gay lifestyle is so seductive, you better believe that once a young man has tasted the delights of gay Paree, he won't be satisfied with much of anything back at the farm. Everything wholesome and normal pales by comparison! Watching football with Dad? Yawn! Family picnics with barbecued weenies and potato salad? Who has time for it? He'll be off partying with his oh-so-gay friends, living it up at pool parties, conversing at highbrow salons and socializing at swank soirées, eating tasty hors d'oeuvres and canapés with caviar while you're stuck mowing the lawn!

"We've got to put a stop to this nefarious plot to seduce our young people into the abominable gay lifestyle. The homosexual conspiracy is a threat to the very fabric of the family! Stop recruiting our kids! Keep your perversions to yourself! Save our children!"

Pope Bans Madonna and Child from Vatican

ROME: A spokesman for the Pope announced that Madonna would be banned from performing her *Passion Play* in Vatican City. "This is an outrageous affront to Christendom," the Holy See said. "We will not have our holiest holiday desecrated by the sacrilegious punkery that Ms. Madonna is so infamous for."

To the consternation of Catholic authorities, Madonna had hoped to put on her new show in St. Peter's Square on Good Friday, but the Pope's denunciation put a stop to that. They feared another impiety, similar to *Like a Virgin*, which scandalized Italy some years back.

"I don't see why they always malign me for making fun of Catholicism," Madonna said. "As a mother myself, I've embodied a new understanding of the sacred bond between a mother and her child. On this holiest of holy days, I wanted to portray the Mother of God's anguish in the face of her ultimate sacrifice. In my performance piece, my child is dressed up like baby Jesus, arms stretched against the cross, while I dance the Passion of Madonna. I fling my arms to the sky, asking 'Why, why, *why* must my innocent child be sacrificed for the sins of the world?'

"It's like a birth/death motif, innocence and loss, sacrifice and redemption—but at what cost? Could a mother reasonably be asked to sacrifice her child, even if it saved the world? My performance reveals and examines that fundamental tension. I act out the incredible Anguish, the Passion, and the Despair of a mother losing her child—even if God demands the sacrifice."

Don't you think Catholics might find your piece a little offensive, even blasphemous?

"Blasphemous? How can you say that? I'm actually a very religious and spiritual person," she insisted. She was attired in a tasteful little outfit of black mourning lingerie, a studded leather choker around her neck, her scarlet cloak wafting in the breeze behind her. "Plus I myself am a Catholic! I seriously don't understand the problem."

After being expelled from the Vatican, Madonna hoped she could play the Colosseum, but Roman authorities barred her show. "This exhibition is in astonishingly bad taste," the mayor said. "It offends the sensibility not only of Catholics, but of all Romans." They refused to give her a license to perform her piece anywhere in Rome.

What's a *Passion Play* without an audience? And how do you get an audience without a venue? This vexing problem chased Madonna up and down the Italian peninsula, as town after town refused her any place to put on her show. Turned away from Venice, Florence, Bergamo, Genoa, Naples, and Verona, banned even from entering the stony Sicilian hilltowns whence her ancestors came, she finally defied authorities and performed her piece on the cliffside of the Amalfi coast.

Her *Passion Play* caused quite a traffic jam for the entire holy weekend as people perched in olive trees on the cliff to capture the sight of Madonna venting and howling her anguish around her toddler, who she'd propped against a small wooden cross. Transfixed by Madonna's passion, thousands swayed to her rhythmic rants, waving their arms and wailing, as the child, seemingly oblivious to the chanting crowd, gazed calmly across the blue Mediterranean Sea.

A Psychic Reading

YOU WERE very sensitive as a teenager, with a profound depth to your personality that others rarely appreciated. You felt that your parents never fully understood you, and other kids at school seemed incredibly goofy and immature. Sometimes you wished everyone would just leave you alone, and other times you felt so lonely you thought you would die.

You have an incredibly creative side that you have never fully developed. You secretly suspect that you're really lazy, and wonder if you'll ever live up to your full potential. Yet, when the chips are down, there's an inner strength in you that will rise to the most rigorous of life's challenges.

You feel self-conscious around strangers, especially if you're attracted to someone. But with the right sort of caring attention and gentle encouragement, you can really blossom!

Once in a while you get in touch with a mean streak, which makes you want to lash out at others, or say unkind things. But even though you can be a little vicious at times, you are still an amazingly generous and caring person!

I can tell that even after all you've been through, you still want the best for everyone. As far as the future goes, you can be anything you want to be! You just have to put your mind to it. Despite your jealousy, you will be successful in love, and I am confident you will achieve your heart's truest desire.

The whole world lies at your feet. The world is a piece of cake, and you're the frosting. All the world's a stage, and you're the star! You are so special!

Vampire Smitten by Werewolf

In a recent interview, following a rash of rumors and a spate of celebrity appearances, Count Dracula finally admitted that his heart had been staked out by a wolfman who roams the steppes and woodlands of Transylvania. He refers to him affectionately as "Woof."

They met under the ghostly glow of a full harvest moon. The Count had been out trolling one foggy evening through his favorite graveyard after slurping the blood of a young maiden, when he heard an eerie howl that spiked the hairs on the back of his neck: "Ahh-rooooo!!"

He cocked his ear to the shrill and sinister bellow. He heard a nasty snarl, when suddenly a shadowy figure leapt out of the gloom, clutched him by the collar, and dragged him down. A fierce fracas ensued as he struggled with the wolf-like creature, his face rasped by rough whiskers, his nose overwhelmed by the scent of musky fur. The werewolf wrestled him to the ground, clamped his jaws on his neck, pinning him to the marble slab, and ravished him.

The Count was smitten. "I love how he growls when I nuzzle his muzzle," the Count explained. "When he knocks me over and tosses me about with the shake of his massive head, he definitely grabs my attention.

"Ever since I met Woof, I've been remarkably lively for someone who's undead. Woof just brings out the zest in me. Especially during the full moon, his voice gets husky, hair sprouts all over his back and snout, and he gets that devilish glint in his eye. That's when I know he's about to rut, and it totally electrifies me.

"Tormented and restless, he turns ill-mannered and rude. He crashes around the castle, roughs me up, and heaves me into the dungeon. Then he lurches off, marauding the countryside, disemboweling sheep and dismembering peasants. He gets so worked up, that when he comes home I can't wait to see him. That's when the real fun begins."

Woof agreed. "Vlad—that's the Count's Christian name—is not someone I'd usually think of going for. He's so refined, with his smooth, pale skin, nicely filed nails and teeth. He wears a high starched collar and a black cloak lined with red satin. And he has such elegant manners, being a Count and all, that I figured he'd spurn me—a rough-mannered woodcutter from the country. But some say opposites attract, so who knew?

"He's a tad shy of the sunlight, so I just let him get his beauty rest in his cute little coffin-bed during the day. But deep in the dark of night, he turns into a ravishing, bloodsucking fiend! When I come home after a tough stint of ravaging the countryside, he nibbles at my neck with his scrumptious love bites, and gives me hickies for days! Then, when we're making love, I howl with delight when he sticks it to me—Ah roooo! I call him Vlad the Impaler." He nudged the Count with his shoulder, and grinned a wolfish grin.

"I never imagined I'd ever find someone quite like Vlad," Woof continued. "I just figured I'd spend the rest of my life plundering and pillaging with little hope of ever finding true love and settling down. But Vlad snatched my heart when he scratched my neck with his long sharp fang, and pierced my jugular. I was his, forever."

The Count took Woof's paw and they gazed fondly into each other's eyes, sweet and winsome as a couple of love-vultures. All through the interview, they blushed and giggled shyly at the sheer joy of finding one another. Overcome with happiness, the Count uttered a bat-like squeak, and Woof sighed with a snarly groan.

The love-sick pair can often be seen long after midnight, in the romantic graveyard where they first met, dancing the Tango cheek to cheek on a polished marble mausoleum, as the blood-red moon rises over the Transylvanian steppeland. "Ah rooooo!!"

Faith No Longer Obligatory, Jesus Says

In an attempt to clarify an age-old conundrum, Jesus said today that faith alone is being reconsidered as the sole criterion for eternal life:

This is a quandary I've been contemplating for some time. I wonder whether it's possible to will faith even for oneself, much less demand it from others. And if you honestly lack faith, should that be considered a character defect? Does it really make sense to hold people accountable for a failure to believe?

These are troubling perplexities that have plagued mankind ever since I left. They have never been satisfactorily resolved, to my way of thinking. I suspect the capacity for belief has more to do with temperament, family background, or one's social context. Perhaps sincere desire can shore up faith, but I question whether mere intention can create conviction out of thin air. Isn't faith something that comes about through grace? (And after all, whose responsibility is *that*?)

Divine intervention, of course, is the old standby—like zapping Saul blind on the road to Damascus, that's certainly one way to compel compliance. But that sort of persuasion can hardly qualify as free will, can it? I have to admit, there was definitely an element of coercion involved in that conversion.

In which case, it seems to me it's not entirely reasonable that access to heaven should be based exclusively on whether you believe I'm your Savior. Because if you don't believe it, then I'm certainly not *your* Savior, am I? At least under the old rules, I'd be more like your worst nightmare, what with the rending of flesh and the gnashing of teeth for eternity.

Under the previous dispensation, you could be quite the scoundrel until the very end as long as you confessed on your deathbed, sincerely repented, and acknowledged me as your personal Savior. So if we do away with the faith stipulation, we'd better shore up the good works requirement. Otherwise, it's a totally free ride—everyone gets in, no matter what! Where's the incentive to be a decent person? And who'd be dying to get into some club that anyone could join?

All I've ever asked is that you believe in me. Should we attribute the absence of faith solely to a willful obstinacy? What about all those pagans who have never been exposed to Christianity? Or other thoughtful people who may have heard of me, but nonetheless remain unconvinced, have doubts, or sincerely hold another opinion. Must a simple lack of faith preclude Salvation?

I've taken up this dilemma with Father. At first He was leery about such a major reversal—how do you reconcile burning all those heretics down through the ages? And hell's presumably chock-full of souls with appeals to consider—what a gargantuan task! But we've got all the time in the world (and then some). It doesn't seem prudent to continue a policy you know is unworkable just because it looks bad to admit a mistake. Even if you are infallible.

Here's an idea. Maybe we could still use faith to encourage repenting, but if you lack faith, you could make up for it by being good and having a kind heart. That way we cover all the bases.

We're planning a chat with that old spook, the Holy Ghost, just to get a consensus. He usually does all the hands-on work by touching someone's heart, moving their spirit, showing them the light—or scaring the holy bejesus out of them! So He'll definitely want to get his two cents in.

But I suspect a new edict will be coming down the pike sooner than you can say "suffering succotash." I figure once every millennium or so it's good to offer another incentive to keep that halo gleaming.

Freshman Tickled to Death in Hazing Incident

YPSILANTI: The body of Sam Yonsky, a freshman at Eastern Michigan University, was found this morning after an all-night roustabout initiation rite sponsored by his *Gamma Alpha Upsilon* fraternity brothers. The coroner noted that the alcohol content of his blood was not enough to account for the sudden death that apparently occurred around 3 o'clock in the morning. Revelers were presumably unaware that Yonsky had passed on to the next realm, as he was propped up at the table with a joker's hat on his head. It was only this morning that it was discovered he was no longer breathing.

Frat brother Jason Curlew was at a loss to explain what might have happened. "We're not like the other frats that get guys drunk, tie them up, then toss them into the swimming pool with a toilet plunger up their butt. Sure, we have our little initiation rites, but we're not into hazing. This is really horrible." Jason was overcome with grief, and the interview was discontinued.

Al Spartan, president of the fraternity, was brought on the carpet at the Chancellor's office to account for this terrible tragedy. "Really, all we did was put on a little entertainment to celebrate our new pledges. Some of the guys recited English poetry and played Renaissance music from the sixteenth century, while others dressed up like the cast of *Swan Lake* and pirouetted around the room.

"As part of the initiation, new pledges were supposed to take turns singing arias from *Madame Butterfly*. Sam got the giggles, and couldn't stop. He got caught in this silent, spasmodic laugh, where he just rocked back and forth. Every once in a while he'd make this ominous wheezing sound when he tried to take a breath. We whacked him on the back to try to shake him out of it, but he just kept rocking. It was scary."

Asked if anyone thought to call an ambulance, he said "No; we were all just laughing and having a good time, no one ever noticed that he'd swallowed his tongue. Maybe the laughing brought on some kind of fit."

The victim tested negative for marijuana use, so stoned giggles were ruled out as a probable cause of death.

When asked whether anyone had purposely tickled Sam, if that was part of their hazing, Al swore "No one touched the guy. Honest. We have a total hands-off policy in respect to initiation rites. We used to tie guys up and tickle their ribs, nuzzle their armpits, lick their feet and suck their toes, they'd laugh their heads off and wet their pants, but we haven't tickled anyone since they instituted the no-touch initiation guidelines."

The Chancellor of the university announced yet another anti-hazing policy, which forbade the use of humor in initiation rites, which henceforward could only include solemn pronouncements, to protect freshman from dangerous levels of hilarity, which could very well burst a vessel or bust a gut, as was evidently the case with poor Mr. Yonsky.

Later, talking to reporters outside the Chancellor's office, Al Spartan suddenly recollected another piece of relevant data. "You know," he said, thoughtfully, "I think Sam must have made some quirky association with *M.Butterfly*, 'cause he kept banging his head against the table as he repeated the phrase, 'How could he *not* have *known?*' "

Man Sues Guardian Angel

TRENTON: The trial opened today in the case of *Robert Goodrich v. his Guardian Angel.* Mr. Goodrich charged his angel with malpractice last year for not coming sufficiently to his aid when an eighteen-wheeler overturned on the New Jersey turnpike, smashing his car. "All these other cars veered outta the way, but my brand new Porsche slid right under the truck. Totaled. All these guys thanking their lucky stars for saving them in the nick of time. Where was my lucky star? Where was *my* Guardian Angel when the going got tough? Nowheresville, that's where. Out to lunch, takin' a coffee break—a lousy slacker, is what he is."

When called to the stand, the angel's feathers were plainly ruffled. He took a seat, folding his wings over the back of his chair. "Used to be, people were thankful for whatever heavenly dispensation they received: if they were crippled by polio or by an accident, at least they could still use their hands. If they lost their sight, at least they could still hear, taste, and feel. If their house burned down and they lost all their possessions, at least their children got out alive. In the old days, we got credit for that. Nowadays, everybody's got a gripe. This guy's car was totaled and he walks away from it without a scratch. He should be grateful it wasn't a lot worse."

The angel's attorney said, "Please tell the court what might have happened, if you hadn't intervened."

"Well, he could have been horribly maimed, for one thing, in a body cast for a year. Or third degree burns over ninety percent of his body, painful skin grafts for months. He might have died in the fiery wreck, his wife killed by the shock, his kids orphaned and placed with his in-laws or abused by foster parents."

"And you prevented that?"

The angel nodded. "I've prevented that and a lot of other stuff throughout his life he never even realized. Like the time he was walking along the top of a fence, even though his mother told him not to, he fell off and scraped his knee. He could have broken his arm, his leg, or his skull, but I flew down and cushioned the blow."

"Yeah, and dragged my knee through the gravel!" charged Mr. Goodrich.

The angel looked impatient, but held his tongue.

With barely concealed contempt, Mr. Goodrich's attorney cross-examined the angel. "A brand new Porsche! Totaled! And you claim my client should be *grateful*? He's lucky it wasn't even *worse*? What about my client's sense of well-being? What about his faith in a Guardian Angel who will watch after him, take care of him, keep a look-out for his best interests?"

The angel tried another tack. "I think there's been some misconception about our true vocation," he explained. "Our mission is to ameliorate misfortune—not to avoid it altogether. It's not within our power to totally eliminate illness, infirmity, or death, which comes to us all."

The plaintiff's attorney interrupted. "But not to angels! Am I right?"

The angel shifted uncomfortably in his seat. "Yes, that's true."

The attorney approached the bench. "Your Honor, may I quote from the solemn Oath of the Guardian Angel?"

"Yes, you may."

He opened a Bible. "This is from Psalms: 'For he will give his angels charge of you to guard you in all your ways, On their hands they will bear you up, *lest you dash your foot against a stone.*'" He slammed the Bible shut. "There you have it, your Honor! My client's faith in a just universe has been utterly shattered! Once lost, no amount of money can salvage it, no belated acknowledgment can restore his peace of mind." The lawyer solemnly gestured toward Mr. Goodrich, who sadly shook his head.

The judge pounded his gavel. "In the light of this outrage to moral justice, all that remains to rectify this affront to humanity is the swift judgment of this court." He turned to the angel and lectured him sternly. "You will reimburse the plaintiff for his Porsche and pay him one million dollars in restitution. You may no longer offer yourself in the State of New Jersey as a bona fide Guardian Angel. I hereby clip your wings and strip you of your Guardian's license. Fallen angel, it's time to turn in your lucky star!"

Mr. Goodrich gloated, while the angel wept.

O.J. Hired as Domestic Violence Spokesman

Los Angeles: Workers in the domestic violence field were appalled when it was announced recently that O.J. had been hired as a spokesman for a male batterer's program.

Linda Galsworthy, spokesperson for a coalition of battered women's shelters, said "We just find it utterly inappropriate for a man who has been successfully sued and held accountable for the murder of his wife and friend, who still denies any complicity in their loss of life, to be chosen as a spokesman for other batterers."

Arriving at the press conference to assert his side of the story, O.J. was visibly shocked by the coalition's response. "I was declared absolutely one hundred per cent *Not Guilty* by a court of law in a fair trial, so I don't see where they get off trying to impugn my reputation by hearsay and the shenanigans of double jeopardy perpetuated by the relatives of the unfortunate deceased."

O.J. went on to admit that at one time he did have a problem with domestic violence. "Yes, I slapped Nicole around a few times, and I realize now that it was wrong. Only sometimes she could be such a bitch, there comes a point you gotta put a woman in her place."

Ms. Galsworthy fumed at this statement. "This is exactly the kind of denial we're talking about! It's typical blame-the-victim mentality, as though a woman deserves to be slapped around, much less murdered, just because she disagrees with him."

When asked what sort of advice he now gives men when they get in trouble with domestic violence, O.J. said "I try to get them to calm down a little bit and look at the big picture. You gotta take responsibility for your own temper. Even if the broad's a bitch, you don't necessarily have to take it on the chin, but you gotta keep your cool. So I just tell them to go out on the ho and bang some other booty to show her who's boss. That way you ain't hurting nobody, but you put her in her place, big time."

Don't you think your message might be compromised by your own past?

"What people gotta realize is, even if I did do something like that? It would only have been because I loved Nicole so very much. And that's the bitter truth." Here he got a little choked up. "I miss her so much, and so do the children. If I ever get my hands on the guy what done that to her, I'll break him in two."

Any theories about who might have murdered her?

"Well I hate to admit it, but Nicole had a little cocaine problem, so I wouldn't be surprised if she got messed up with some dope-dealer dispute. She always could pull a fast one, and some dude finally got pissed off. Can't say as I blame him, if she jerked him around like how she done me. Not to say it wasn't wrong, but you mess with drug dealers, and yo' ass is grass."

O.J., you were a model for millions of boys, who wanted to grow up to be a big football star just like you. What advice would you give young men nowadays, who are just starting to date?

"Well, first of all you gotta realize that your girl is not your property, and she's not always going to agree wit' you. Sometimes you got to reason with her, you can't just force her to go out with you, go down on you, what have you. You got to treat her nice, bring her flowers, tell her how pretty she looks. If she still won't put out, then you're perfectly within your rights to whack her upside the head."

At this point in the interview, Ms. Galsworthy became incensed. "That is absolutely disgusting!"

O.J. held up his hands and said, "Just kidding. Can't you take a joke?"

"I don't care if you are just kidding, that's a horrible thing to say! And you're giving advice about domestic violence to young men? This is an outrage!"

"Yeah, well okay, you're right," O.J. conceded. "That was way outta line. Truth is, if your woman don't want nothin' to do with you, you just gotta walk away, no matter how much it hurts you inside, you got to swallow your masculine pride and realize you can't force anyone to love you. That's the bitter truth I finally had to learn the hard way."

Harry Potter and the Temple of Doom

FORT LAUDERDALE, FLORIDA: Focus on Love and Understanding for the Family (FLUF) has called for a boycott of Disney to protest their upcoming movie of the *Harry Potter* books. "The Sorcerer's Apprentice in *Fantasia* was bad enough, but at least it demonstrated the folly of indulging in the Occult," a spokesperson said. "With Harry Potter, you've got witchcraft and sorcery glorified, so every kid's going to start dabbling in Satanism, casting spells, and evoking Demonic Powers!"

Harrison Mustang, chosen to play the wise wizard, Obie Won Pinocki, said he thought the boycott was overkill. "Our movie is just good fun, challenging kids' imaginations," he explained. "We're simply following the age-old myth of the hero's quest: answering the call to adventure, the hero's character is sorely tested. At the climax of the story, he slays the dragon and brings home a boon for all of mankind."

But the spokesman for FLUF insisted that more sinister forces were at play. "What you airily dismiss as 'mythology' is actually camouflage for pagan religion! This story is full of violence and curses. It glorifies the forces of Satan! Deuteronomy tells us, '*There shall not be anyone among you . . . who uses divination, who practices witchcraft, or who interprets omens; or a sorcerer, who casts a spell . . . For whoever does these things is an abomination to the Lord!*' "

Mustang tried again to explain, "Our movie doesn't promote sorcery, any more than the story of Merlin does in the King Arthur legend. It's really a fairly innocent coming-of-age adventure with fantastic, magical qualities, like *The Sword and the Stone*."

Mrs. Garbel, a mother who protested the reading of Harry Potter books in her daughter's second grade class, echoed FLUF's concerns. "I don't want to come home one day to find my child's bloody body, sacrificed in some ritual by a Satanic cult! We want to make sure no mother has to cry into the TV cameras, 'Why, oh *why*, didn't somebody *do* something to *stop* this!' "

The FLUF spokesman added, "What disturbs us the most is that the Lord's name cannot even be whispered beneath one's breath, while Sorcery and Witchcraft are allowed to flourish in every classroom across the land! Satanism is a diabolical religion, and our kids are being brainwashed by the Occult!"

Tommy, 11, couldn't understand what all the fuss was about. "Don't these grownups realize that sorcery isn't real?" he asked, somewhat bewildered. "It's just make-believe, like *The Wizard of Oz*."

"You don't understand the demoniacal nature of the forces you're playing with here," the spokesman warned. "And quite frankly," he sniffed, "we really don't care much for Dorothy, or her odd assortment of friends, either."

Reporter Covering Right's Reaction to Gay Marriage Loses It

MONTPELIER: The state legislature today approved a new bill granting gays and lesbians the right to marry. Vermont's governor promised to sign it, causing an expected uproar across the land.

"We will never recognize gay marriage!" swore Davy Doolittle, member of California's state legislature. "It's immoral, it's sacrilegious, it undermines the family!" and all the other whiny gripes we've heard over and over again in this never-ending dispute. I just hope the Supreme Court cans every one of the states' anti-gay marriage laws, just like they did with anti-miscegenation laws back in the 'sixties.

Oops, that's not very objective reporting, is it? But sometimes a reporter's gotta do a little editorializing, or he goes bonkers, the same old ridiculous claims and homophobic diatribes—Good God, what's going to happen next, are we gonna let Joe Shmoe marry his dog?

And what kind of example are we setting for our children? My Lord, what would happen if they saw people who actually loved each other form a committed relationship? The family faces imminent destruction! We're going the way of Rome, or Sodom and Gomorrah! Every great civilization that's fallen because of its inner corruption, all caused by men giving each other a wank—Oh, please. You'd think the sky would fall in, the way they carry on about it. If I recall, Rome didn't fall until *after* it converted to Christianity. Light that cigar and puff on it.

The truth is, these homophobes are afraid their own kids will start getting bright ideas. Once they know gays can get married, why, they'll all want to become gay, too! They already copy every gay fashion that comes down the pike, so what's next? If you give any legitimacy at all to these perverts, the next thing you know they'll want to marry your son. Everyone knows they're out to recruit every kid this side of Hoboken into their sordid lifestyle—and maybe your own son will turn gay just to spite you!

Well, we've all heard this claptrap before, and frankly, I'm weary and bored with it. Maybe I'm burnt out covering the Bible beat, and I need to take a breather by reporting on mineral extraction, or Serbian iconography. My editor says I gotta get a grip, if I can't maintain a more objective tone about these episodes, he's gonna transfer me to the Guinea pig-caught-in-the-plumbing beat.

But these self-righteous, Bible-beating, blathering idiots really goad my gizzard. Why the next thing you know, they'll be claiming that all gays want to do is piss in their coffee and give them AIDS. As if they didn't have better things to do, like get on with their lives. These nut-cases should get a job, get a life, get a wife! Every repressed desire in their own misguided disgruntlement gets projected onto gays, it's all so transparent, it's ludicrous. Like the old canards that the *Negroes are gonna rape our women*, and the *Jews are gonna eat our children*.

Yeah, right. Everyone knows what gays really want more than anything else is to suck on some straight guy's dick, who in any case usually just lays back and enjoys it, like who really gives a fuck what gender your mouth is? A blow job is a blow job.

The Literaturization of Life

Every intelligent painter carries the whole culture of modern painting in his head. It is his real subject, of which everything he paints is both an homage and a critique. —Robert Motherwell

WHILE THE MIST swirled against the window, I looked for an empty spot among the crowded tables at Cafe Flore. Abandoning my search, I resigned myself to sitting outside in the fog, when a man reached out and touched my arm. "Jack, isn't it?" he said.

"No, it's Charles."

"Charles; right." He removed his foot from the other chair at his tiny table, and said "Have a seat." I sat down with my coffee and took off my coat, trying to place him. He was dressed all in black, with colored splotches of paint up and down his thighs. Then I remembered we'd met at a loft party south of Market a few months ago.

"You still painting?" I asked.

He clasped his hands under his chin. "To tell you the truth," he said, "I'm tempted to let it go." It seemed he was having an early midlife crisis: his last show had barely broken even; his art had turned arid; his life, meaningless. He was tired of the constant shmoozing, the trite hypocrisy of the whole gallery scene. Cocaine, and even women offered only temporary respite from his ennui. "Sex is like grinding away in this existential void, you know what I mean?" I wasn't certain that I did, but not wanting to go there, I just nodded.

"I've seriously considered the Golden Gate Bridge." He tilted his head, with a rueful smile. "Only it's so cliché." I supposed at such a desperate time, he wouldn't want anyone to think he was caught in clichés. "But just walking into the ocean—back to the primal source—it has a poetic sense of return, don't you think?" I looked through the haze at a woman with white-frame sunglasses, smoking a cigarette with ruby-painted lips.

"You know what your trouble is?" I said, at the risk of offending him. "You're too caught up in the image of the *artiste*."

"Tell me about it," he said, tilting his wine glass. "I can't put one slash of paint on the canvas without stepping back and analyzing whether that slash was influenced by the minimalists or the expressionists, Picasso or Dada. It's incredibly inhibiting. I wasted five years in art school learning about everyone else, when I should have been trying to find my *self*."

"Where did you lose it?" I asked.

"Through intellectual dissipation," he said. "We're so out there, when what's really happening is *in here*." He clasped his fist to his chest and thumped it, twice.

The woman with the sunglasses blew a smoke ring.

I stirred my coffee, and said "Your situation reminds me of a concept in German, called *die Literaturizierung des Lebens*."

"Oh, really?" he said, leaning forward. "What's that?"

"It means the literaturization of life—trying to live as though you were a heroic character in a romance."

"Oh wow." He slapped the table. "Don't I know that! It's like I'm walking around in a bad novel, and I can't find my way out."

"Must be pretty rough."

"Incredibly," he said. "You know, sometimes I think about throwing it all in and moving to the country—fresh air, trees, real people—I've gotten to the point where I'd seriously consider it, I really have."

I looked at his hair, flowing in a half-bleached cascade down one side of his head, shaved over his ear on the other, a dragon tattooed on his neck, a ruby stud through his nose, and a safety pin piercing one eyebrow. "Nature," I said.

"Exactly! None of this urban, hyper-sophistication. Sweating out in the sun, smelling the leaves; chugging a few beers." He slung his arm over the back of his chair.

"How would you earn a living?" I asked.

"I don't know. Live off the fat of the land, like the Indians. Sleep out under the stars, keep warm by the campfire."

"Rustle some cattle now and then," I said.

"Sure; whatever. Just so long as it's real."

I finished my coffee and pulled on my coat. "I've got to get going. Take it easy."

"Hey, we'll see you around, Jack."

"Charles," I said.

"Whatever. It was great talking like this. It's a fresh perspective; it really is."

I nodded and took off. As I walked down the street in the heavy mist, I pulled my jacket close to my chest. I shuddered to think I might have been responsible for preventing a perfectly understandable, even heroic, suicide.

Gays Start Their Own Boy Scout Troop

Berkeley, California: It was announced today that several gay boys have gotten together to form their own Boy Scout troop, defying the national leadership, which forbids gays in Scouting. The National Council immediately denounced the move, and threatened to sue them over the use of the name Boy Scouts.

Jimmy Bashford, 14, Senior Patrol Leader, said "We don't really care if they recognize us or not. And we're not going to get into some big fight about the name. We're calling ourselves 'Gay Scouts,' and there's nothing they can do about it." Asked what sort of activities they had planned, Jimmy enthusiastically described their program:

First of all, we're getting rid of those tired old khaki uniforms. For everyday campouts or doing good deeds, we're wearing black shorts and boots, with silver lycra T-shirts, and black berets. For dress up, like at parades or award ceremonies, we'll put on dark Armani blazers, with a Lambda monogram. And you can wear whatever silk scarf you like, to add a little color.

Forget the old ranking system: Tenderfoot, Second Class, First Class, Star, Life, and Eagle. We kept Star, of course; that's what we start off with: *Everybody is a Star in Hollywood!* From there, it's Aurora, Galaxy, Pulsar, Nova, and Super Nova. And if anyone's bad, he gets sent to the Black Hole for a spanking.

We've also instituted some new merit badges: Fashion Design; Haute Cuisine; Opera Diva; Knots and Kink.

As ever, a Gay Scout is trustworthy, loyal, incredibly helpful, very friendly, courteous to a fault, kind even when dishy, fairly obedient (if pushy), cheerful, not terribly thrifty, awfully brave, exceptionally clean, and a tad irreverent.

On my honor, I will do my best to do my duty to my community, and to obey the Scout Law. To help other people at all times, and to keep myself physically strong, mentally awake, and morally—upright.

When we go camping, we hike up to the waterfall and skinny-dip in the pool. Then back at camp, we cook up a storm: baby arugula salad, porcini mushroom soup, fettuccine al fresco, rack of lamb and roasted vegetables with wild rice, a flambé of chocolate mousse for dessert. After dinner, we really camp out. We bring out the disco music, feather boas, lip-syncing drag queens, and strip-tease go-go boys. Then it's lights out, time to practice our knots for the new Bondage and Submission merit badge.

We're planning a series of community service projects: re-decorating the senior citizens' retirement home; baking cookies for snack-time at the nursery school; and starting a quilting bee at the local hospital.

Basically, we're just a bunch of wholesome, red-blooded American boys out to serve our community and have fun! We want to develop our citizenship, promote environmental stewardship, and provide a little enjoyment to share our gratitude for our own good fortune with the wider world.

The Second Coming

THEY CALL ME JC2 because I was cloned from the DNA of Jesus. These mad geneticists figured they'd make a bundle on the Second Coming, so they stole a sample from *Il Prepuzio di Jesu Cristo*, a holy relic kept in the Cathedral of Carpata, just north of Rome. It's his foreskin. Really, I'm not making this up. To authenticate the source, they compared the genes from his foreskin with a blood sample from the Shroud of Turin. I know, many scholars claim it's a hoax, but millions of people believe it's genuine. Lo and behold, it had the same DNA. So I'm supposedly Jesus incarnate, the Son of Man, the Lamb of God. But of course I'm not really Jesus, just his twin.

Still, being such a close relative is quite a cross to bear. People have all these unrealistic expectations—like I should have a direct line to Dad, our Father who art in Heaven. Believe me, I've tried: I've prayed, I've wandered through the desert, I've withstood temptation, but no communication yet from Pop.

I don't have any parents. Of course there was this sheep who carried me to term, but she was just a hireling, not my real mother. True, she was a virgin, but they didn't want some cult of Dolly (or Little Bo Peep) taking over the program, so they decided to keep her in the background. Who raised me were Bill and Jeff, the guys who cloned me. They called themselves the Replicators, and they had in mind a very specific trajectory for my life.

I don't give a rat's ass about fulfilling some prophecy. Maybe I have the same genetic material, but I'm no Savior. I just want to have a good time—be kind to my neighbors, sure—but also look out for Numero Uno. The sins of the world are not my problem—my brother took care of that the first time around. The only skin I'm interested in saving is mine.

What really got Jesus into trouble was going up against the Romans—bad idea. Bill and Jeff likewise raised me to take on this deified role, like the Pope or the Dalai Lama. The pomp, the glory, the abject adoration by hysterical masses, the Thousand Year Reign, the Lake of Fire, the Final Judgment. To say nothing of being mistaken for the Antichrist and hung up on some cross again, no thank you.

When I was seventeen, the reps were about to present me to the world and claim credit for the Second Coming. (They decided to wait this long because they couldn't imagine anyone worshipping some pimply-faced punk into heavy metal, tongue studs, and tattoos.) But I escaped and hitched across the country, landing in this wacky California commune, a bunch of Jesus freaks searching the sky for some comet to take them on to the next level—yikes! Then I shaved my skimpy beard, got a haircut, and tried to blend in with the rugrats skate-boarding through the mall. My handlers were frantic, of course, having lost their ticket to wealth and glory, but I don't think they really understood what we'd be in for.

Since then I've lived a fairly quiet life as a carpenter. Through the grapevine, I hear these loony Replicators are still tracking me. Since I'll soon be thirty-three, they're getting desperate.

I've let on to my union buddies I've had a few tax problems, so when anyone comes snooping around asking questions, these guys let me know about it. How long can I hold out before some Judas sells me down the river? Not that anyone's on to me, but my handlers can be pretty persuasive. I'm seriously considering a career change. What can I do? I never went to school, and sure I can multiply a few loaves and fishes, turn water into a fair vintage of wine, but at least till this millennial frenzy blows over I need to keep a low profile.

JFK Jr. Discovered on Desert Island with Princess Di

IN AN AMAZING development that has rocked the world, John Kennedy Jr. and Princess Diana were found together after eloping to a tiny island off Barbados, where they've been living quietly ever since faking their tragic, early deaths in the late nineties.

Asked why they had chosen to deprive the world not only of their company, but of the happy news that they had found each other, they both cited the strain of leading such rich and openly public lives.

"I grew weary of always having to keep up appearances," the Princess complained. "After the divorce, all the tawdry confessions and so on, I just couldn't tolerate any more public scrutiny. It became unbearable."

John, America's own prince, nodded. "Our lives bore a certain resemblance in a lot of ways. Both of us contributed what we could, but in the end it was difficult to live up to all the expectations. Being young, wealthy, and strikingly beautiful has its own challenges, but to be famous as well for no particular reason takes its toll. It's not as though either of us had ever really accomplished anything.

"As celebrities, we became targets for the world's projections, even though we're quite simple folks with our own foibles and traumas. Failing the bar exam and Di's eating disorder only served to make us seem more human, and thus more appealing and likable. It's a terrible burden, really."

"I think it was the lack of privacy, in the end, that made me want to fake the accident and flee," Diana said. "It's true that I sought out a certain level of attention, but it became self-perpetuating. It gnawed at me, the way people fawned over me. One can only take a certain amount of abject adoration."

John said, "I could hardly jog across Manhattan in my shorts and tank top without teenage girls or gay guys swooning at my feet. It got a little embarrassing. Diana had been languishing in Barbados, waiting for me to join her, but I had to find the right moment. When my wife insisted on flying through the storm to Hyannis that weekend for my cousin's wedding, I thought this was the perfect chance to get away."

How could you possibly have faked your own deaths, when they found your bodies?

"All the public saw was photos, and as we all know, photos can be faked," John said.

But your family came to identify you.

"When you're a bit mangled or water-logged, it's amazing what can be done to convince even close family members. No one really wants to take a very careful look. They weren't even real bodies."

And what about Di's sons?

"Leaving my sons to Charles would have been my greatest grief," Diana said, "and I never could have pulled this off had I been permanently separated from them. But both boys have been brought here secretly to stay with us a few days at a time. Charles and what's-her-face are so preoccupied with each other they don't really notice. Frankly, they'd just as soon be rid of the little princes, but they have to keep them around for the sake of appearances. And one day, William will be King—perhaps even bypassing Charles." She brightened at this happy prospect.

So what happens now that the Prince and Princess have been rediscovered?

"I suppose there's no getting away from it all," Di said. "We'll be in the limelight for a while, but this time it won't last long. Everyone remembers us in our thirties, still in the blush of youth, yet mature enough to command a certain authority, which neither of us really deserved. Now that we're a little older, our looks are beginning to fade and I'm afraid we'll be a bit of a disappointment. That's one advantage of dying young."

John agreed. "Who needs people traipsing after you all the time with their jaws sprung? It's really not that much fun, and when it finally drops away it'll be no great loss. We'll just go about our business. I'll join a law firm or some start-up e-zine, and Di will keep up with her charities, but I really don't expect people to hang on every word we say anymore or photograph every move we make."

Speaking of photographs, what about the spread that's about to appear in Hustler *magazine that shows the two of you romping naked through azure waves at the coral edge of your idyllic island hideaway?*

They both shrugged. "Faking one's death can be a spiritual awakening," Di explained, "because you really move way beyond some of these mundane concerns."

But what about the photo? Will you sue Larry Flynt, or try to suppress the shot?

"It's only flesh," Di said, "and flesh is so temporal."

John, nuzzling his Princess, said "I couldn't agree more."

Kimberly

One Sunday afternoon I was contemplating my troubled existence—laid off my job as a group-home counselor, the rent due, with Sean, my ex-boyfriend, stalking me—when the phone rang. I thought it must be him, and was going to ignore it, but then I decided to tell him the police were tapping my phone and the next time he called I'd have him arrested.

"Hi!" the voice chirped, "I bet you'll never guess who this is!" She was right. "It's Kim Fulcher!" The only Kim I could recall was this beefy, red-haired guy I met in a club south of Market, who wanted to arm-wrestle me at the bar for a blow-job.

"You know, Kimberly, from Mrs. Sherman's class!"

"Oh, Kimberly." I vaguely recalled the girl who sat next to me in the sixth grade.

"I thought you might live around here, so I just called directory assistance, and Bingo! There you were!"

"How about that."

"I'm right across the bay, so we're practically neighbors!" Since I didn't respond right away, she asked "So, are you married?"

"I'm gay."

"You're gay! I should have known. You know, I had the biggest crush on you in the sixth grade, did you ever realize that?"

Week after week, I'd come home from school with bruises on my shins. My mother tried to reassure me by saying "That's just how girls show they like you."

"And—guess what? The first man I married turned out to be gay. Isn't that something? What a cowinky-dink! I really know how to pick 'em, don't I?"

"I guess." Not that my record's any better, when I think of the speed freaks and assorted maniacs I've dragged home over the years. But I try to learn something from each encounter: No more boys on the rebound. No manic-depressives off their lithium. No stalkers. I'm slowly making progress.

"We have a thirteen-year old son, who now lives with his father, and this guy I was dating, a former minister, told me he didn't think a teenage boy should have a fag for a father, so I told him to take his holier-than-thou homophobia and shove it."

I warmed up to her a little when she told me that, but I was still wary.

"So what are you doing now?" she asked.

"Uh, nothing much. I got a lot to do around the house, today. You know, laundry and so on. For the work week."

"Not *right* now, you silly. I mean what do you do for a living?"

"Oh, yeah. Well, I'm going to grad school in the fall. Assuming I get in."

"Oh I'm sure you will. You were always so smart. What are you studying?"

"Psychology."

"Oh, thank God for psychology! After my divorce I went into therapy and decided it was do or die, time to really get my act together. So I put myself through law school working nights at this horrible pastry sweatshop in east Oakland, and I passed the bar on my very first try, quite an accomplishment for a single mom thank you very much. Then I got hired by this hot-shit corporate law firm that made me work seventy, eighty-hour weeks evicting poor, undocumented tenants from over-priced slums until it totally ruined my health and I had to give up my son, I told you he lives with his father? The gay one? So I went on disability and sued the bastards and now I live in the house I paid for with cold, hard cash from the settlement. I was determined to get my own place, which no one could ever take away from me, so that's why I paid for the whole thing. In cold, hard—oh I already told you that. Which I got from the settlement."

"Uh huh."

"Oh, listen to you, Dr. Freud, you sound just like a psychotherapist! I can tell you're studying psychology. 'Uh huh,' that's what they always say! Now I bet you're going to ask me how I'm feeling."

"No, but I wonder how much you've been drinking." I can spot the monologue of a lush a mile off.

"Ha ha! I had that one coming, didn't I? You sound just like my psychiatrist, only he says drinking is definitely not my biggest problem. Do you drink?"

"No," I lied.

"Take any drugs?"

"No."

"What are you, some kind of Mormon? How do you get by?" she sighed.

She caught me up on how Glenda, one of our head cheerleaders, had married an evangelical Marine, and the other one, Miriam, had turned into a broken-down whore. "Really, that's how she supports herself, the poor dear. And Lawrence Stanza, the captain of the football team, the one who became student body president? He got thrown in the hoosegow because he gave horse tranquilizers to some teenage girls!"

"So what are you doing now, Kim?"

"I'm still on disability, but I do pro-bono work for the homeless."

"That sounds like an important job."

"Well how could some rich, white male possibly comprehend what it's like to live on the street, is what I'd like to know. You sit there in your cushy, rent-controlled apartment and laugh all the way to the bank! La de la de la!"

"I've worked with some homeless people."

"Oh, I am so sure. In your liberal, do-gooder way you've Done Your Part for the Homeless!"

"Listen, Kimberly, it was—"

"I bet you even give them a quarter when you pass them on the street!"

"Look, it was nice talking to you, but I got to get going."

"Oh. Well. I guess I said the wrong thing, didn't I? Got under your skin? A little too close to home? I'm sorry, I'm sorry, erase that. I take that back. Can I take that back? Is it all right if I call you again? Here, I'll give you my number, so you can call me. You can call whenever you like. Night or day, hell, sometimes I can't even tell the difference. You got a pencil?" She gave me the number. "Now read it back to me."

"I got it."

"No, you have to read it back to me! I can't stand wrong numbers!"

"Kim, if I got the wrong number, you wouldn't even—"

"READ IT BACK TO ME!"

I read it back.

"That's area code five-one-zero."

"Got it."

"Call me! You promise?"

"Goodbye, Kim."

Erase that? Yes, if only we could edit our conversations with the same ease we press the delete key. I'd like that for myself, and try to give others the benefit of the doubt. With Sean, anything you said could be held against you. He'd provide enough rope to hang yourself, and no, you couldn't take it back, ever. That was the climate toward the end of our relationship, where a grudge was nursed like a Venus fly-trap in a hothouse of mutual suspicion.

Two minutes later, the phone rang.

"Hi, it's me."

"Yes, Kim."

"I'm sorry if I attacked you about the homeless, it's just that so few people really understand their plight, and then you have all these politicians using them to get rich on programs that never do diddly squat for the people who really deserve the help, and I didn't want you to think any less of me because I lumped you together with all those other bastards. I'm sure you're not really like that, only I think it's about time America finally woke up and got its shit together and SMELLED THE FUCKING COFFEE!"

"No hard feelings."

"Call me?"

"Bye."

The phone rang. Oh, great. Now I had Kimberly stalking me, too. I lifted the receiver and hung up. It rang again. I grabbed the phone. "Kim, get a life, godammit."

Not missing a beat, the voice on the other end said "Who's Kim, you little slut—your new girlfriend?"

It was Sean.

Leni Riefenstahl Champions Gay Aesthetic

GENEVA: Leni Riefenstahl, notorious for her film, *Olympiad*, shot during the 1936 Olympics in Berlin, announced on her 100th birthday that she applauds the gay aesthetic, which demonstrates an unabashed appreciation for the male physique.

"*Olympiad* was way ahead of its time. I filmed male athletes at the peak of their power, representing the ideal masculine form, which hadn't been celebrated since the Renaissance, or the Golden Age of Greek civilization. Critics sneered—my film was dismissed as a 'fascist aesthetic,' whatever that's supposed to mean, just because I staged some events and Hitler used my footage to legitimize the Berlin Olympics. To glorify the nude male was seen as somehow demeaning to men.

"Now you've got all these gay boys photographing each other getting all buffed and hunky. Who but gay men could so thoroughly revel in male beauty?"

What about the feelings of men who don't measure up to the ideal male form? Why not represent a wider view of masculinity?

"It's *Art* we're talking about here, not anthropology! Yet my career has covered a vast range of images—my work with the Nubians should vindicate me from any charges of proto-Aryan leanings left over from *Triumph of the Will*."

But aren't you contributing to gay men's internalized oppression by promoting glorified images that no real guy could ever aspire to?

"Do gay men fetishize hunky guys only as a reaction to previous oppression?" Ms. Riefenstahl countered. "Or are they lusting after an ideal expression of masculine beauty, 'cause that's what they're in to?

"Look at the fashion magazines, underwear ads, and even gay porno! It's all about hunky, muscular guys, because that's what we all want to see. Women admire strong, muscular men; boys aspire to be just like them; gay men lust after them; and even straight men like to think of themselves as being way more muscular and masculine than they really are. I'm only reflecting what people want."

Then aren't you just pandering to the vulgar taste of the masses?

"One minute I'm a fascist elitist, the next minute I'm pandering to the hoi polloi! I'm not the sole arbiter of aesthetic taste. We've always had female nudes that everyone admires; I've simply done my part in liberating a new aesthetic appreciation for well-developed men. Go and shoot underwear ads with hairy beer bellies if you want to, just don't expect them to stop traffic in Times Square."

Ms. Riefenstahl, you learned how to scuba dive when you were ninety years old, stunning the art world with your underwater photography. Now that you've reached a hundred, what's next?

Leni covered her mouth to hide her girlish grin. "Nude skysurfing."

Bad Boy

HELLO, LINDA? . . . It's me, Mary. I met this total dream boat . . . At the probation office, wouldn't you know. He was arrested with a couple of friends who were involved with this burglary, but he claimed he wasn't part of it . . . Of course that's what everybody says, I've worked with enough offenders to know that. He wouldn't turn state's evidence because he's loyal . . . I'm not saying I believe it, I'm just telling you what he said!

He wears this tight black T-shirt. He's tall and very athletic. His long black hair falls over his eyes . . . Chinese, of course. His name's Danny . . . I am not a cradle robber! He's thirty-five years old. I know, all these underworld characters have names like Sammy Lee and Joey Wong and Danny Ho.

What attracts me is that he's trying to get his life together . . . What do you mean, that's not all that attracts me? . . . Well, he took the civil service test for the post office, so he's trying to get a regular job and be responsible. But now that's in jeopardy—he's still on probation, plus he recently was arrested for driving while under the influence. He claims it's his first one . . . Of course he's in denial . . . Me? I'm the one who's in denial? . . . I'm not! . . . Oh, you're probably right.

Of course I shouldn't go out with him. I told him no, it's totally unethical, I could lose my job. I happened to go to the park for lunch, how could I help it if he ended up on the same bench? It's a free country, right?

He was sitting on the back rest and I sat between his legs . . . Not facing each other! Anyway he reached down and kissed my neck and then my lips and slipped his hands into my blouse, and I said "Not here, you crazy man, you'll get us arrested!" He was so brazen! He just grinned at me and said "You want to sleep with me don't you?" I said, "You haven't even taken the HIV test."

Yes, I would, but only for fun. Except that night, I kept thinking about him . . . Oh it would never work. First of all he's not even financially stable. He drinks too much, he has a criminal record . . . Yes I know he's trying to be good, but Trouble with a capital T is written right on his forehead . . . Okay, I already admitted that's why I like him. All the other Chinese men I've dated lately are so sedate and conventional and boring. They sit in front of their computer screens and print out money . . . I know it's a stereotype. Even I'm a lot more traditional than I let on, that's just not what I'm attracted to. That's the problem. How do you get security and excitement in the same package?

He asked me to marry him! What could I say? I laughed. "You don't even know me. You couldn't possibly love me." He said, "I know, but I could grow to love you. We'd have such cute children." I said "If they looked like you." . . . I wasn't! . . . Okay I admit I was flirting, but it wasn't anything major. Then he said, "Nah, if they looked like me they'd be ugly. But if they looked like you!" . . . Yes! He wants to settle down. I think he'd make a good father. At least on the nights he wasn't out gambling with his friends.

You're right, I should forget him. Please remind me not to call him. I never should have gone to the park during my lunch break . . . I suppose I would, if he called me . . . No, we'd just go out . . . Nothing would happen! . . . Well even if it did, it could never develop into anything serious . . . I told you, we're too different. I wish I could just have a fling, only I can't let myself go unless I'm fond of someone, and I don't want to get too fond of him.

I think he's more interested in me than just that . . . I'm being naïve? He doesn't really like bad girls. He says he stays out of trouble when he's with a good woman. He's attracted to women who look after him . . . No he doesn't have a mother complex, Ms. Psychoanalysis!

I know. Whenever you agree with me that he's totally bad news I think up all these nice things about him . . . So why don't I just sleep with him? Now you're playing reverse psychology. Because he's unstable, he drinks too much, he's in denial about his criminal past, and he has rowdy friends. How could I bring him home to meet my family? My father would croak. He probably hangs out with hit men in Chinatown, for all I know. The other night his cousin wanted him to teach some guy a lesson who had a beef with this other friend Danny had never even met . . . That's what I said! It's so dangerous, and what business is it of yours, anyway? The next day he told me he thought better of it. You see? He does have some impulse control.

He went out last week to this benefit jazz concert for the Asian American Dance Company, which he claims he wanted to invite me to, but it was sold out. He met someone there and since I wasn't available, what was he supposed to do? . . . Well I know I told him to back off. Whose side are you on? Linda, he even got it on with one of the women guards when he was in jail. Right in his cell! . . . Yes, they have women guards, so I don't think he's lying. But why would he tell me that, anyway? He is so narcissistic.

No, I'm not going to call him . . . That's right. He'd have to call me, which he isn't going to do because he senses I'm not right for him. And even if he does, there is just no way . . . I'll simply tell him I could never go out with him. It's impossible, it would never work. Besides, I'm not even interested.

[Click, click]

Hold on. [click]

Oh hi Danny! Just a second. [click]

Linda, it's him! I'll talk to you later . . . I know. He's trouble. He's a sociopath. He's a drunk. He's in denial. He's bad. He only wants one thing. I'll call you tomorrow. [click]

The Summer My Cousin Turned Mormon

My cousin Robby came to stay for two weeks every summer. I looked forward to these visits with mixed feelings. Being a year older and more rambunctious than I was, he would draw me into intrigues I was too timid to try on my own. Once we got into it, I allowed myself to be carried along by his enthusiasm and imagination. Robby embellished our explorations with tales of daring heroism in the face of untold dangers—gale-force winds, sinking ships, mountain rescues, or beating off pirates in the pursuit of treasure.

In reality, our gambits were never terribly outlandish: previous expeditions included sliding down grassy hillsides on pieces of cardboard to escape the dinosaurs (I got stickers in my butt); climbing up the ivy on the side of a small cliff to rescue a maiden (I broke my arm when the vines tore); slashing our way through underbrush to build the Panama Canal (the poison oak made my face puffy and my eyelids swelled shut. I looked like a radiation victim from a horror flick, and itched terribly for days in the most sensitive places).

Despite discomfort and occasional trauma, these escapades provoked only mild consternation in my mother, who would shake her head and wonder what had gotten into me, had I taken complete leave of my senses? But she never forbade us to go off on our adventures. She probably thought our exploration was a healthy challenge to my self-restraint, and she saw Robby as a fairly benign influence on my boyhood.

The summer I turned thirteen, however, everything changed. Robby was bigger, his voice had deepened, he was sprouting hair in ungodly places. My own body had barely begun its strange alterations, and I was both intrigued and repelled by the changes in his. The previous summer he had hinted at forbidden pleasures—smoking, sneaking a beer, messing around with some girl. I had looked forward to seeing him, although I was nervous about what sort of schemes he might lead me into now.

But rather than becoming even wilder, ready to go, he seemed oddly subdued. It was hard to draw him out. He was dismissive of any ideas I had of fun; he'd outgrown it all. Of course neither of us cared anymore about GI Joe or trains. But even swimming, horseback riding, or going "exploring," which in the past would have sent us racing out of the house, now evoked a sneer. I was crestfallen. How could I relate to him? And I was frankly angry with him for not leading me into illicit arenas—drunkenness, abandon, and sexuality—I was too reticent to explore on my own.

My mother would try to get us out of her hair, asking cheerfully "So what are you boys up to today?" Not wanting to be scorned for my suggestions, I'd defer to Robby, who mostly shrugged.

"I don't know," I'd finally say. "Maybe just hang out." We'd drag ourselves to the mall and look over the newest releases at Tower Records, but nothing seemed to get us going again.

Then late one night, I heard this strange thumping noise and yelling coming from the den. We had a sofabed that Robby slept on, backed against my bedroom wall. I heard more thumping, and occasional yelps. I made out "Stop it! Stop that! No! No! No!"

Fearing an intruder had attacked him, I got out my baseball bat and was about to charge into his room, when I swore I heard him singing *A Mighty Fortress is Our God.*

I knocked on his door. "Robby?"

"What? What?"

"I heard some yelling. Are you all right?"

"It was nothing. I'm fine."

"Are you sure? Can I come in?"

"I'm fine. I'm fine. Go away."

"Did you have a nightmare?"

"I said I'm fine! Go away!"

My mother came out in the hall. "What's the matter?"

"Nothing. I think Robby had a nightmare."

"Is he all right? What are you doing with that baseball bat?"

"I thought I heard someone yelling, but he says he's fine."

"Well okay. Goodnight, then."

I went back to my room and put the bat away. Something was up, and I had to get to the bottom of it.

The next morning Robby was his usual sullen self. I wanted to contrive some way of getting him out of the house so I could case his room. Not normally a sneak, I rationalized that I had the right to discover the source of my cousin's betrayal, as well as his puzzling behavior—for his own sake, if not mine.

After Mom left for work, I gave Robby a gift certificate for Macy's I'd gotten from our grandmother for my birthday, and said he could take my bike and get anything he wanted—I had enough clothes, anyway, and besides, I had to do some chores around the house, like washing the windows and scrubbing the kitchen floor. Not wanting to help me, he quickly agreed. I was surprised my ruse worked. Then I kicked myself for piling it on, since I'd committed myself to a hell of a lot of drudgery—but I wanted to make sure I got him out.

I watched him take a spin out of the driveway and coast down the hill. Then I got some Windex and paper towels and went into the den. I searched through some drawers, but he'd never really unpacked. His suitcase lay open with clothes piled on either side. As I rummaged through them, I wasn't sure what I was looking for—some girlie magazines, maybe, or a porn video—but I did not expect to find the *Book of Mormon*, which I spotted lying underneath the bed, along with *Overcoming Masturbation—A Ten-Point Guide to Self Control*, distributed by the LDS Church, plus a little calendar, in which day after day had been totally blackened with deep, dark ink.

I poured over this Mormon tract with fascination. "Masturbation is a sinful habit that is totally self-centered and secretive, and in no way expresses the proper use of the procreative power given to man to fulfill eternal purposes . . . This self-gratifying activity will cause one to lose his self-respect and feel guilty and depressed, which can in the extreme lead to further sinning."

It went on with a series of suggestions for overcoming this terrible habit:

1. Pray fervently and out loud when the temptations are the strongest.
2. Yell to stop those thoughts as loudly as you can, then recite a pre-chosen scripture or sing an inspirational hymn. (Ah ha! *A Mighty Fortress*, indeed.)
3. Take a small pocket calendar and if you have a lapse of self-control, color that day black. (I looked at his calendar, and smirked.)
4. If you are tempted to masturbate, think of having to bathe in a tub of worms, and eat several of them as you do the act! (Yum!)
5. A *Book of Mormon*, held firmly in hand, even in bed at night has proven helpful in extreme cases. (No doubt.)
6. Tie one hand to the bed frame, and wear several layers so you cannot easily touch your vital parts.
7. Never associate with other boys who have the same weakness. YOU MUST BREAK OFF THEIR FRIENDSHIP! Just to be in their presence will keep your problem foremost in your mind.
8. Do not admire yourself in the bathroom mirror. Leave the door open when you bathe, and never stay in the bath more than five minutes. THEN GET OUT OF THE BATHROOM!
9. Never read about your problem. KEEP THE PROBLEM OUT OF YOUR MIND BY NOT MENTIONING IT EVER, NOT EVEN IN YOUR PRAYERS! Keep it out of your mind!
10. Remember, Satan never gives up! You can win this fight! The joy and strength you will feel when you do will give your whole life a radiant and spiritual glow!

The previous summer, Robby asked me if I ever beat off. Looking back on it now, I realize it was probably an invitation. But at the time I'd never done it, and being the literal-minded boy that I was, it sounded a little painful. "No," I said, dubiously. Then to explain why I hadn't tried it, I told him "I think if you have any tendency toward homosexuality, it might make it worse."

Robby looked shocked, and quickly changed the subject. And although I wasn't especially attracted to him, I was enormously curious, and would gladly have participated with him that summer. Now it was too late. If I even hinted at it, I would no doubt be banished.

But what had happened to him? What caused this mysterious shift from the adventurous boy who'd try anything, to this sullen teen given to yelping and singing hymns to keep himself from self-abuse?

I quickly put everything back where I'd found it, and proceeded with my chores. My mother was amazed when she got home. "What's come over you?" she asked. The windows gleamed, the kitchen floor was spotless. "You poor thing, you must be bored out of your mind."

She didn't know the half of it. Robby came home and actually seemed somewhat cheered by the hooded 'Niners sweatshirt he bought at the mall. My mom took us out for pizza, then we went to see this movie called *Sliding Doors*, about a woman who misses her subway train, gets mugged, and goes home to her boring boyfriend; then she suddenly splits into what would have happened if she'd caught the train after all, got home in time to discover her boyfriend with another woman, and left him for the romantic stranger she'd met on the subway.

We chattered about this movie all the way home. In one split second, your whole life could change, and we played the "What if . . ." game trying to imagine what your life would be like if it went this way or that.

"Well my life would have been infinitely worse off if I hadn't become a Mormon," Robby finally confessed. It was out in the open now, and though I dreaded the subsequent proselytizing, I asked him what had changed him.

He said he'd gotten into smoking pot and running around with a rough crowd, and if it hadn't been for this one girl in his class who had shown him the *Book of Mormon*, he's sure he would have become a juvenile delinquent. But now he had a purpose, to serve God, and all his bad habits had fallen away.

Except for one that I had some secret knowledge of, but of course I held my tongue. I wanted to catch him at it, maybe even do it with him, and was a little horrified by my own scheming.

That night, I lay in bed wide awake and totally turned on in anticipation of Robby giving in to temptation. Finally, I heard his tell-tale thumping, and then his husky voice barked out: "Eat worms! Eat worms!" I leapt out of bed, tore down the hall, and threw open his door.

"What? What are you doing!" he cried, squinting at the light, pulling the blankets over him. I grabbed at his covers, which he tried to hold on to, but since he had one wrist tied to the bed frame, I yanked them out of his grasp. His pajama pants (and the swimsuit he'd put on as an extra barrier) were shoved past his knees. He covered himself with the *Book of Mormon*. "Leave me alone!"

For a moment I hesitated. My God, what was I doing? I didn't mean to torment him, but to free [illegible] both from our self-imposed restraints. So I said "Look!" and parted the fly of my pajamas to show him my hard-on. He stared at me in astonishment. "Let's color this day black!"

My heart pounded as Robby considered my suggestion, and I prayed that he wouldn't scorn me. He leaned against the pillow, eyeing me with suspicion. Then the slightest grin turned the corner of his mouth as he put aside the *Book of Mormon*. He nodded toward the hand he had lashed to the couch. "Untie me, then."

So I did.

Oedipus Denies Complex: Sues Freud for Slander

THEBES: In a startling development, Oedipus the King denied having an *Oedipus* complex, and filed suit against Sigmund Freud for slander. While admitting that he killed his father and slept with his mother, it was never his conscious intention to do so:

That Viennese goofball got everything mixed up. My father Laius, the King of Thebes, stabbed my foot when I was an infant, and left me for dead with the express purpose of avoiding this terrible prophecy. As fate would have it, I was rescued from the wilderness and reared in Corinth by King Polybus, who I assumed was my real father.

After the oracle at Delphi predicted I would kill my father, I ran away from Corinth to avoid hurting Polybus. On my way to Thebes, some pompous jerk ran over my swollen foot with his chariot, so I killed the bastard. Then I answered the Sphinx's lame riddle and won the right to marry Jocasta. How was I to know she was my own mother?

It's obvious that King Laius was paranoid—suspecting I'd kill him and steal his wife—talk about projection! Where this Freud fraud gets off claiming I'm the one who really wanted to kill him just doesn't square with the facts—it actually colludes with my father's delusion.

Dr. Freud claims this was all unconscious. Yeah, right—so if I'm not aware of wanting to kill my father and sleep with my mother, that pretty much wraps it up. It's a classic case of circular logic.

Let's set the record straight. Sure, maybe I had a little rage about being abandoned, who wouldn't if your father tried to get rid of you? But I didn't know the stranger who crunched my foot was my father—I was merely defending my honor.

Then later, a terrible famine came upon the land. To end the famine, the oracle said the murderer of the King must be brought to justice. I searched high and low to discover who killed King Laius. Imagine my surprise when I found out it was me! And the King was my true father! And Jocasta, my queen, was really my mom!

Once I knew the truth, of course it seemed too weird to continue on as husband and wife. She's free to see other men and I'm sure one day I'll fall in love again myself. The kids still live with us and we're basically a happy family.

All this malarkey about how much better I can *see* since I blinded myself. Yes, I admit I was blind to the truth, but I never poked my eyes out. I actually thought the entire episode was pretty funny. The very steps my father took to prevent this calamity, actually brought it about. How ironic! Poetic justice, really. And the famine's over, so where's the gripe?

Should a twist of fate form the foundation of psychoanalytic theory? To turn the story of an irascible paranoiac who tried to get rid of his son into a complex of unconscious patricide and incest goes way too far. If I ever get my hands on that coke-head quack I'm going to throttle him.

No, I won't take the law into my own hands. We'll see Dr. Freud in court. He'd better retract his libelous slander or he's going to pay through the nose.

One-Minute Marriage

IN TODAY'S BUSY WORLD, it often seems impossible to set aside sufficient time to meet the demands of an insistent spouse. However, in the long run, one must examine one's ledgers to weigh whether a moment here or there might not save the inconvenience of a hasty divorce, to say nothing of an expensive settlement. Time is money! Money is time.

Harpies and nay-sayers decry the intrusion of management techniques into the sacrosanct realm of romance, as if removing the veil of connubial ambiguity would wilt interpersonal passion at bloom's first blush. Twaddle! No one expects business partners to allow weeds of petty acrimony to put a strangle-hold on the roots of mutual enterprise; nor should one anticipate anything less from Marriage by Objectives.

Au contraire—young urban professionals throughout the nation enjoy high profit margins of emotional satisfaction from clearly managed contractual relationships. What's clear is accountable; what's countable is clearly advantageous to you and your partner.

We have developed an enticing array of easy-to-follow, human-oriented mechanisms for clarifying roles and expectations (such as, "Who's boss?"); and for gracefully handling those awkward moments when it's difficult to simply agree to disagree.

Naturally, initial attempts toward marital efficiency may take more than a minute of your time; but with practice, you will find that you can soothe a prickly spouse (or avert an expensive dissolution) with a Sanguine Smile, a Consoling Remark, or (if necessary) an Arched Brow.

Take a moment from your hectic schedule to consider the conjugal cost-effectiveness of a One-Minute Marriage. Why leave reasoned negotiations to the board room, when they might serve an equally salubrious effect in the bedroom?

Satan Behind Witch Craze, He Admits

SATAN admitted today that he was behind all the witch crazes down through history, but not quite the way everyone assumed:

Yah, it was my idea, right from the start. But I never held a Black Mass, I never caroused with witches, I never had anyone bewitch a cow, or send their familiar out to torment their neighbor. No demon of mine ever possessed anyone's soul.

No, what I did is set the whole thing going by simply planting the notion that Satan was behind every unfortunate occurrence—sickness, crop loss, or hysteria. What could be more diabolical than that? What's the need for any real witch, when people are perfectly capable of creating witches out of ignorance and fear? You start twitching from a little anxiety, then you think the devil's got into you, and you panic, big time. Then you blame whoever reminds you of your own forbidden impulses. You bewitched me!

You want sex? Blame it on a witch, who came to you in the shape of an incubus or an alien, and seduced you. Did you let your crops rot? It's Satan's hand, not your own lazy soul, or just bad weather. Did your child die? Your stocks go down? There must be someone to blame!

It doesn't even have to be a witch, per se. It can be a communist or a homeless person, out to grab your hard-earned cash; a homosexual, out to seduce your children; a Satanic child-care worker, conspiring to molest your babies; an alien, come to snatch your fetus or your sperm; an immigrant, sneaking across the border to nab your job.

I get everyone going, pointing fingers at each other, until they work themselves into such a frenzy that the scapegoating turns into real violence—the Jews are rounded up, the homosexuals are bashed, communists jailed and immigrants expelled, the witches are burned! You think you cast down Satan and triumph over evil when you burn a witch? That's my ultimate Glory!

After a while, they go too far. Even upstanding citizens are caught in the web: powerful people who themselves participated in the hysteria, are finally accused: the police are part of the Satanic cult conspiracy, the army is full of communists, the judge's wife is a witch. Then it all falls apart, as people gradually realize they've been tricked again, frightened by their own shadows.

Ha ha! So now you know, for all the good it will do you. There are no demons possessing you, no witches with unearthly powers, no succubi or incubi to seduce you, no aliens to take you away and probe you in their spacecraft—they're all your own phantasms, flickering in the night.

Even I am as insubstantial as a shadow. I'm gone as soon as you switch on the light. I have no real power, no control—my only clout is the diabolical leverage you permit me.

Brunhilde

AFTER WORKING several years at a mental health clinic, I decided to start a private practice in psychotherapy. I left my position and put an ad in the local paper, hoping clients would start rolling in. After several weeks, I hadn't gotten a single response; it gradually dawned on me that quitting my day job had been a big mistake. In short, I was becoming desperate. One day, while considering whether to go crawling back to my old job, the phone rang.

"I loved your ad!" A woman's voice, full and resonant, exclaimed. "It sounds smart, hip, and so with-it! It was succinct, to the point, and if I may say so, brilliant!"

"Well thank you," I said, not sure where this was leading.

"This is a revolutionary approach, and I can tell you are someone who is going somewhere!"

I was flattered to think my ad appealed to someone—anyone. I had suggested a focused, problem-solving approach to overcoming blocks which I thought was a helpful angle, one that I believed in. "I wouldn't call it 'revolutionary,' exactly—but I think it's a good, down-to-earth style of therapy."

"It's bold! It's creative! It's cutting edge! I'm an excellent judge of character, and my intuition tells me that *you* are a *genius*. If you play your cards right, you have the potential for greatness!"

I have to admit it was gratifying, in this rough and tumble world, to have someone reflect my own hidden wish to be viewed with such grandeur. At last, someone recognizes my true potential! I imagined basking in the limelight of adulation. But of course she didn't know me from anyone, so I was determined not to be taken in by such fulsome praise, as I tried to figure out what sort of scheme she had in mind.

"Do you mind if I ask who you are?"

"I am Brunhilde, publicist extraordinaire! I have helped scores of talented people, such as yourself, attain the distinction they deserve by the correct placement before an adoring public. I can get you on all the radio talk shows, as many magazine interviews as you could possibly handle—and TV! We're talking Good Morning America, here—Dateline, 20/20, the Tonight Show, and best of all, *Oprah*! Where I have personal connections."

I thought it was fitting that she had such an operatic-sounding name to match her vision. "I see, Brunhilde. And how much do you charge for these services?"

"What I provide is priceless! There is no way you could ever properly evaluate the value of my *entrée du jour*. My only satisfaction is in seeing others rise to the height of their true magnificence!"

"And what, exactly, does that come to?"

"I've had dozens of wannabe celebrities begging, pleading, offering twenty, thirty, forty thousand dollars to take them on, but I won't do it, not unless I see the same potential I see in someone such as yourself. I wouldn't waste their money, and I certainly wouldn't waste my time. If you act right now, all I ask is a modest retainer of ten thousand to begin, and with the amount of exposure you'll be getting, that's a minuscule price to pay. After three months, if you're not entirely satisfied, you'll get back every single dime!

"But that's just the beginning! By the end of three months, you'll be direct-depositing a small fraction of your transactions into my account every week. A pittance, compared with what you'll be earning! And not a penny out of your own pocket! Only a paltry percentage for my modest efforts. Just send me a certified check for ten thousand dollars, and a voided check authorizing automatic withdrawals from your account. I'll send along your notarized, guaranteed contract, and we can get started."

"I'm afraid I don't have that kind of money lying around."

She paused for a moment, then said, "May I ask you a personal question?"

"What's that?"

"Are you satisfied, now, with the level of business you're bringing in on the basis of this ad?"

"Not really."

"Well surely you can beg, borrow, or steal! A man of your stature has the means, I have no doubt about that. Put it on your credit card. You can't let this opportunity pass you by!"

There was some small part of me that was mildly intrigued—if only a tenth of what she said was true, if she could really get me that kind of exposure—and the fact was that I hadn't been doing all that well on my own, despite my belief that I really had something to offer. Of course she already guessed this, it was what she was counting on. I loathed self-promotion, and the idea of letting someone else take it on sounded very appealing. "Could I have some references from previous clients?"

"References! If I gave out the names of my clients it would violate their confidentiality! Surely that's something you must understand in your own line of work."

"Well perhaps you have contacts in the media I could talk to."

"Excuse me, but my contacts happen to be extremely busy professionals who cannot possibly be bothered with suspicious, faithless nose-abouts sniffing into other people's business! I put my faith in you! Haven't I just explained what I could provide?"

"Still, I don't really know you."

"Nor do I know you! But I'm willing to trust my intuition that you're a winner! I saw your ad, and I thought, here's a man who knows what he wants and how to get it. Am I wrong about that?"

"I guess it would help to know a bit more about who I'm dealing with."

"And I thought you were a champion, a trail-blazer! Well maybe I was mistaken. Maybe you're just a big old Loser with a capital L who couldn't recognize the best opportunity in his life if it came along and smacked him in the face! But I don't think I'm wrong! You just don't have enough faith in yourself. Don't you deserve to make the best of your life, to overcome the blocks that are getting in your way to achieving the kind of success you deserve?"

I thought how clever that she's using concepts from my own ad to gull me.

"And you'd let a measly ten grand get in the way of attaining your life goals? Isn't your future something worth investing in? Aren't you worth more than ten thousand dollars?"

"I'd feel more comfortable if I could see your track record."

"Oh, you'll see my track record, all right. Didn't I promise you'd get back every single dime of your initial investment if we didn't bring in another eighty to a hundred thousand dollars worth of business? It's in the contract! That's a thousand percent, guaranteed! What kind of risk is that?"

"Why do you object to giving me some references?"

"Don't insult me. I've already explained to you, if you would only listen, the only risk you're taking is to pass up an absolute bonanza! For what? Because you're scared. You're a scared little boy who can't see past his nose because you think the bogey man's gonna get you! Who needs a security blanket to help you through the night—well let me tell you, buster, there are no security blankets in this world. If you're looking for absolute safety, total comfort, then just stay home and never dare to venture out into the real world!

"But with this proposition, you're risking absolutely nothing! If you can't seize a golden opportunity when it's offered to you on a silver platter, then I just don't know what."

"I must be about the biggest loser you've talked to all week," I said.

"But it doesn't have to be that way! Expose yourself to the world—your audience awaits you! You'll never, ever, regret it. The only regret you'll have is if you pass up this chance, simply out of fear, the same baseless fears you help your clients overcome! I believe in you! You're not even risking a dime, it's all guaranteed! You just have to believe in yourself! You have nothing to lose but your own blinding fear. Send me that cashier's check for ten thousand dollars by next-morning FedEx, and we'll be on our way to a new and glorious day!"

By this time, I'd heard more than enough of her hustle. "Well, thanks anyway."

"Don't miss out! You'll regret it! Maybe not today, maybe not even tomorrow, but next week, next year, and for the rest of your life! You'll always wish—"

"Goodbye."

After I hung up, I still felt a twinge, even though I knew she was a blowhard and a con. I was a vulnerable mark, eager for recognition (and a paycheck). Maybe she really could advance my career! She sounded so sure of herself, whereas I was wracked with self-doubt.

How skillfully scam artists hook into our uncertainty, our yearning to be acknowledged and respected. Who among us doesn't feel under-appreciated? We'd love to believe anyone who sees this vast potential in us that, once unleashed, would amaze the world.

Should Santa Claus Be Banned?

THE CHRISTIAN CONSORTIUM is up in arms over *The Santa Story*, the new children's book by Agnes Tic that compares God with Santa Claus.

"We are outraged over the profane effrontery of this author to undermine the faith of little children by comparing belief in Santa Claus and the Easter Bunny with religious faith in the Almighty!" the spokesman said during a recent stormy press conference.

The story starts out with a stern warning from *Santa Claus Is Coming to Town:* "Santa can always tell what you're up to—he even knows when you're awake or asleep. And he keeps track of all the times you've been bad, so you better watch out!"

Then it says, "Some children still believe in Santa Claus and the Easter Bunny, and maybe you do, too. But one day you'll suspect it's all make-believe—you realize that fat man could never slide down your chimney, or fly through the air on a sleigh, and of course no bunny ever laid an egg! Well, God is like Santa Claus for grownups!"

The story goes on to show how Jenny and Jamie finally convince their parents that many Bible stories, such as Adam and Eve, Noah's Ark, and the Virgin Birth, are make-believe, too. God is just like Santa Claus, and you can pray all you want, but He never really comes to town.

The book makes the case that we all need to grow up and get on with our lives—being kind to one another, not just so we can get some goodies or go to heaven, but simply because it works out better that way for everyone.

Understandably, this doesn't sit well with the Christian Consortium. "It's one thing to keep religion out of the schools, but it's quite another matter to ban God from the nursery! This is Godless propaganda at its worst!"

Contacted for comment, Ms. Tic laughed and asked, "What would 'Godless propaganda' look like at its *best*?" She acknowledged that *The Santa Story* is a little preachy, but certainly no more so than the picture books typically sold in a Christian bookstore. "Even at Borders, you'll never find anything that questions belief in Santa Claus, much less God. It's one of the last taboos," she said.

At the press conference, a reporter asked the spokesman how he would distinguish Jesus from say, the Easter Bunny.

"Well, we're talking about an entirely different species of faith! Children, once they reach a certain age, can let go of the Easter Bunny when they realize their parents were hiding the Easter eggs all those years. But you can never expect them to relinquish their belief in the Resurrection!"

"What about Santa watching over you, telling Santa what you want for Christmas, trying to be good—isn't that a lot like praying?"

The spokesman seemed caught off guard, then shifted his stance a bit. "Well to tell you the truth," he said, "we don't really approve of Santa Claus, either."

The reporters looked puzzled, trying to grasp his meaning.

"Because Santa just confounds the issue," he added quickly, "as proven by this atheistic blasphemy. We would just as soon get rid of Santa Claus, along with Christmas trees and the Easter Bunny because of this type of confusion."

The reporters gasped.

"All these pagan influences desecrate the true meaning of Christmas! So no, Virginia, there really is no Santa Claus, but that doesn't mean there isn't any Jesus!"

This admission caused quite a stir in the press corps—the Christian Consortium denouncing Santa Claus? It seemed a tad un-American. Another reporter asked, "Would you actually ban Santa Claus?"

"Well, if you ask me do I think it's appropriate for Santa Claus to be in the classroom while Jesus is left out in the cold, then yes, I think it would only be fair to take Santa Claus out of our schools."

This same reporter, who now had tears in his eyes, asked, "No jolly old St. Nick with his Ho, ho, ho?"

The spokesman pursed his lips and shook his head.

"No more Peter Cottontail, hopping down the bunny trail?"

"No, I'm afraid not. That's blaspheming Easter."

"How about *The Night Before Christmas*?" he asked, his voice catching.

"No. It celebrates Santa, and totally ignores the Christ Child."

"No more angel on top of the Christmas tree?"

"No, the tree promotes pagan idolatry."

"No more *Jingle Bells*? Or *Chestnuts Roasting on an Open Fire*?"

"No. We've got to be consistent here. Only *Hark the Herald, We Three Kings,* and *Silent Night*."

The poor reporter was openly weeping by now. "No more Santa Claus coming to town?"

The spokesman paused for a moment, then said "Look, it's not some jolly old chubster coming to town you've got to worry about—it's the Lord, with his flaming Sword!" Then, out of the blue, he broke into a bizarre rendition of the old Christmas jingle: "He knows when you've been naughty, if you're bad He can always tell, He knows when you've been jerking off, so watch out or you're *going to hell*!"

Overcome with sadness (and a bit rattled by this peculiar parody), none of the reporters could bear to ask any more questions. They just shook their heads in sorrow.

"You've got to realize, *Santa* is actually an anagram for *Satan*," he hastened to explain, but the disillusioned press corps turned their backs and slowly drifted away, leaving the spokesman standing in the rain.

Scene from a Marriage

—Doorbell rings. Mia answers it.

MIA: Oh my God. What are you doing here?

WOODY: We need to talk.

MIA: Talk! You have a lot of nerve coming here.

—He pushes his way past the door, comes into the room, followed by a film crew.

MIA: What are they doing here? You can't just barge into my house—I have a restraining order!

WOODY: I know I know I know, I know exactly how you feel, I don't like this any better than you do, but we have to talk.

MIA: I have nothing to say to you! If you have something to tell me, have your lawyer call my lawyer.

WOODY: Listen to me, this isn't something—

MIA: No! I'm not going to listen to you! Get out of here right now or I'm calling the police!

—She lifts phone. Woody grabs her arm.

MIA: What are you doing? Let go of me.

—He takes phone and replaces it on the hook.

WOODY: They're making a movie about us.

MIA: What movie. Who's they? Give me the phone—

WOODY: So we have a choice—we can either be in the movie and give our side of the story, or they'll take it all from the news footage and make a mockery of us.

MIA: A mockery! How could they make any more of a mockery of our marriage than you've already made of it!

WOODY: We're talking TV movie of the week here: "Incest Begins at Home." Is that what you want?

MIA: Me? Is that what I want? How can you even ask such a thing?

WOODY: They saw *Husbands and Wives*, and thought it was so ironic that it should come out in the middle of our custody battle.

MIA: Ironic!

WOODY: So they figured, this is just like a Woody Allen movie, why don't we get them together, bygones be bygones, and have them act it out for us.

MIA: Act it out!

WOODY: Well you know. In a film. Just like old times. Only it would really be our story: Mia miffed at Woody for schtupping her daughter.

MIA: You are totally insane! I can't believe a word I'm hearing! After using me for twenty years—

WOODY: Now hold on—you have a lot of nerve, after accusing me of child-molesting, and you say that I've been using you!

MIA: You are such a beast, without human feeling! You seduced your own daughter!

WOODY: She's not my daughter!

MIA: Well she is MY daughter, and the sister of your children!

WOODY: How can you say I'm being inhuman? Weren't you the one who suggested we go ahead and work on another script after you had just filed child-molesting charges? And you give me this Valentine with pins stuck through the heart? If you want to know what's sick, that's really sick.

MIA: I cannot believe we're having this conversation! It's right out of one of your movies, only it's not funny. It is damned pathetic, if you ask me. So what are they proposing to do, interview us on camera so we can each give our view of what happened between us?

WOODY: That's an idea! Sort of a modern day Roshomon. But we'd also have to interact—run into each other at court, accuse each other, have a dialogue just like we're having now.

MIA: Is nothing sacred to you? Obviously not the bond of father and child—

WOODY: Listen, none of that is really the point!

MIA: That is precisely the point!

WOODY: What I mean is we'll each have the opportunity to give our side of the story, and if we don't they'll basically say whatever they please and make both of us look totally insane. Is that what you want for the children?

MIA: What I want for the children? Is that all you're concerned about, is your image? Your children can go to hell in a handbasket, and I'm responsible for making us look foolish?

WOODY: I thought we could behave like a couple of mature adults and discuss this matter rationally, but apparently you have this thing about being the aggrieved party that you can't let go of, no matter what consequences it might have for you or your career or the effects on the children—

MIA: Since when have you given ANY thought to how all this would affect the children?

WOODY: Oh, now don't give me that! You put up our daughter, and then our son, trying to make me out as a child molester, poisoning their minds with rot that couldn't be further from the truth!

MIA: You ARE a child molester! What are you doing with your own daughter?

WOODY: She never was my daughter! Look, I can understand that you feel hurt and disappointed—

MIA: I don't think hurt and disappointment approach anywhere near the complete and utter devastation I am experiencing this very moment! Hearing you stand there and try to justify and excuse yourself for the most utterly vile, depraved and barbaric treachery!

WOODY: I think you're overstating the case—

MIA: I am overstating nothing! If you could do that to your own daughter, what am I to imagine you might try with the rest of your children?

WOODY: Okay, I rest my case, I have proven my point.

MIA: What point? That you're an unfit father?

WOODY: You'll have the chance to make your point in the movie, or would you rather some idiot wrote your lines for you?

MIA: If I recall, some idiot wrote every single one of my other lines.

WOODY: All right, I deserved that. I'd write it myself, only I wanted to be fair.

MIA: How kind of you to be so thoughtful and fair-minded.

WOODY: I don't think this situation calls for sarcasm.

MIA: You would actually want to act together again in a movie about what has happened between us?

WOODY: My analyst thought it would be very cathartic for both of us.

MIA: Your analyst!

WOODY: We'd both have a chance to tell our side of the story and get it out of our system. It would be just like any other Woody Allen movie, only with the poignancy of knowing that this was really our lives.

MIA: You amaze me.

WOODY: They always assumed every movie we made was about us anyway. How they snickered at our last film!

MIA: Woody, they would simply assume we had staged this whole thing. No one would ever believe that we could possibly act in the same movie after what has happened between us, unless—

—He looks away, thoughtfully.

MIA: Oh no. I get it! If we each told them what really happened, they wouldn't believe it was real! It's just another Woody Allen movie! That's exactly what you want, isn't it? Isn't it!

WOODY: You are so devious in your thinking. You are a genuinely paranoid person. I used to think I was the paranoid one in the family, but you take the cake. You really do.

MIA: Oh, no you don't. You're not going to turn this around on me! That's just what you want—back together again telling the true story of their divorce. And all across the country, people would be nodding their heads realizing what a media blitz we'd put over on them. A new hit, based on the amazing true story of incest, voodoo, and revenge in the custody dispute of the century! All to save your ass at the box office.

WOODY: What do you take me for? I make an honest proposition to work together again, as professionals, mind you, I don't care whatever personal feelings you might have, you can hate my guts, I understand that, but to assume that I would EVER, ever use this story as a way to make a buck or further my career, absolutely astonishes me.

MIA: It astonishes you.
WOODY: Absolutely.
MIA: Well I'm absolutely astonished that you're astonished.
—*Woody nods to cameraman.*
WOODY: Okay, boys—let's call that a wrap.

The Boy Scout's Guide to Masturbation

IRVING, TEXAS: The Boy Scouts of America is sorely peeved over a pirated edition of the *Boy Scout Handbook*, which includes graphic descriptions of self-stimulation in a new chapter called "Masturbation for Boys." At a press conference today, their spokesman summarized their objections:

In our authorized manual, yes, there is a subtle acknowledgment that some boys will occasionally indulge in such a practice, but it balances this observation with good advice for mental hygiene, such as partaking in rigorous sports, praying with your minister, or preparing for your Citizenship Merit Badge. These are wholesome activities that help boys abstain from loathsome habits.

However, this deceitful edition goes much too far in offering specific techniques for this vulgar affliction. It's one thing to recognize that boys will be boys, but it's quite another to provide pornographic depictions of self-abuse! Must we expose our youth to such disgusting portrayals of deviant conduct? Under the heading, "Tricks for your Dick," we found choke the chicken, bang the banjo, beat the bishop, and pump the pud—plus wanking, beating, jerking, and jacking off! Is this really necessary?

To say nothing of a recommended list of various lubricants easily found around the home, such as cooking oil, whipping cream, bacon grease (!), Crisco, butter, or, in a pinch, guacamole! It even advocates ransacking your mother's cupboard for her Jergen's *Lotion*! What must she think if she suspected you were using her lotion for such a dirty deed? How could she ever touch her lotion again? How could she even bear to look at you? And how could you dare to face her, smiling your boyish smile? No, you would have to *hang your head in shame!*

Listen to this promo from the book jacket: " 'The Jizzum Trail' provides a handy section on removing cum stains from pajamas, sheets, T-shirts, underwear, towels, Boy Scout handkerchiefs, and nylon slips." (!) This is outrageous!

Look at these depraved section titles: Extending Your Orgasm, When You're About to Come, Shooting Your Load, and Diddle Your Butt! My God! Is there no limit to such gross indecencies?

And what tops the list of this perverse guide is an entire section called "The Buddy System—how to get off with your friends." It promotes various methods for mutual masturbation, including erotic massage, frottage, and even oral sex! Why, this aids and abets unnatural acts and could actually incite experiments with overt homosexuality!

What is most sinister about this unscrupulous scandal is that this plagiarized manual could fall into the hands of a credulous, impressionable youth, beguiled into believing that this degenerate deception represents the true sentiments and recommendations of the Boy Scouts of America!

Imagine for a moment a suggestible boy trying out some of this advice, touching himself to stimulate his private parts, stroking and breathing harder till he's about to come, then shooting his load in a frenzy of orgiastic pleasure! All the while assuming these nasty pranks have the whole-hearted support of our respectable organization! Untold damage will be wreaked on susceptible youngsters, once they are exposed to this diabolical fraud!

Protect our young men from this ungodly corruption! Keep our boys morally straight! Save our innocent youth! BAN THIS ABOMINATION!

The Man Who Had a Dragon Growing Inside Him (a fable)

ONCE there was a man who had a dragon growing inside him. It was just a little dragon, but the man was Alarmed. He went to the doctor and said, "There's a dragon growing inside me!"

The doctor looked at him in a patronly way. "You've been worrying too much," he said. "These things have a way of working themselves out."

His stomach got bigger and bigger. He became frantic, and told all his friends about the dragon. "How am I going to get rid of it?" he cried.

His friends dwindled.

He became more anxious as the dragon kept growing. He could feel its hooves reaching down into his legs. Its nose began to nuzzle his voice box. His voice began to change.

He began pacing the floor at night. He became accustomed to lighting matches and eating them. His wife left him because of a wild gleam in his eye. His children decided to move in with an uncle from Brooklyn.

He contemplated cutting open his stomach to drag the monster out of him, and lay in a heavy sweat all night long, thinking about it.

The next day he got up and stretched what he thought were his arms, and glanced into the mirror only to discover the Dragon staring back at him! He was startled at first, quite on the verge of ranting. His eyes were fearful. He could not bear to look. He cringed.

He finally worked up enough courage to look again. The dragon was still there. Suddenly, he thought he saw a very familiar feature in his image.

The dragon winked.

After a while he waved his wings, blew a little fire, and wagged his tail. He was okay.

He called up the doctor. "I am a dragon!" he exclaimed.

"I think your ulcers will go away now," the doctor replied.

He gave a party for all his friends. They stood around talking gaily. He told amusing anecdotes, and they drank a toast to him.

The children came home and rode on his back as he flew through the air. His wife came back to him, and said even if he was a dragon, he was kind of cute.

Needless to say, the dragon lived as happily ever after as one could expect, given the circumstances.

Why Do Good Things Happen to Bad People?

IT JUST doesn't seem Fair that people who play by the rules often get stomped on or left behind, while those who lie and cheat seem to come out ahead, does it?

But, do they really win? Just because they're successful and famous, have lots of power and money, doesn't mean they really won.

Do you want to know why? Because love is not in their hearts, that's why. And you can bet your booty that when they go to bed at night, they don't rest with an easy conscience because they *know* that they've been *bad*!

No matter how much the world bows at their feet, no matter what awards and recognition they achieve, they know in their heart of hearts that they are *wrong*.

They may not realize it yet, but they're going to hell when they die, while all the rest of us sit up in heaven right next to God and gloat at their misery forever, Amen.

Ruffled Feathers

I RECENTLY STEPPED into the exotic world of birding: full of exuberant songs, visual delights, and ecological concern. But behind the pastoral facade, I soon discovered that birding can evoke intense passions and contentious disputes. A birding squabble can make a cock fight look like a tea party. The rancor raised by such a ruckus can linger long after the dust has settled. A birder can brood for months at imagined slights, to say nothing of slander, a slur, or a jibe. And it takes far more than a mere apology to smooth a birder's ruffled feathers.

Bridgett, a woman in her sixties, heads the San Francisco bevy of Birds by the Bay. Decked out with a fisherman's jacket to hold various maps, fieldguides, notepads, and pens, she wears a broad jungle hat and lunges through the bush with a forceful, rocking gait that takes some effort to keep up with. Suddenly, she'll stop still as a pointer and peer through her fieldglasses, then announce the sighting of another threatened, if not endangered, species: a brown pelican, a blue heron, or a snowy egret. She's on a mission to document the aviary ecology of the entire drainage system of northern California.

Jacqueline, more tentative and somewhat near-sighted, tends to focus on what's right in front of her nose. She often discovers coot tracks in the mud, and ground nests.

Reilly, an older gentleman from England, gazes through his binoculars with obvious delight and comments frequently on the specimens he's caught in view: a cormorant, a quail, or a hawk. He feigns obliviousness to whatever storms may be brewing around him.

Norma, a matronly woman with a pinched nose, often cocks her ear and cries out, "Hark! A lark!" Sometimes it's difficult to know if she's really being serious.

Although Reilly was the only one from the United Kingdom, his three fellow birders also drifted toward English accents.

We set out the other morning to explore the shoreline of Tomales Bay at Point Reyes, where the rushes fairly bristle with bird life. As we walked along the grassy pathway lined with purple irises, Reilly stopped short, scanning the reeds. "I spy—a teal-crested saddle back!"

"Isn't that a kind of fish?" asked Jacqueline, doubtfully.

Bridgett said, "No, you're thinking of the stickleback."

"Where is it? I can't see it."

Reilly pointed. "There it is, between the rushes."

Suddenly it took off. "Whoopsi daisy!" Bridgett said. "There, it's gone. You've missed it!"

"Oh, pshaw!" complained Jacqueline. "I so wanted to see one."

Bridgett said, "Too bad for you. You'll have to pay closer attention next time."

We made our way through the reeds, when Norma cocked her head and pointed a finger in the air. "Hark! I do declare, a red-winged thistle cropper!"

"Where?" Jacqueline asked, determined this time not to miss it.

"It's close by," Norma assured us. "I heard its distinctive call: 'hoo-hoo, hoo hooo!' "

Bridgett sneered at her claim. "A red-winged thistle hopper hasn't been seen in Point Reyes for over fifty years."

Norma, undaunted by her skepticism, said "Yes, they're quite rare."

"But where is it?" Jacqueline asked again.

"It's beyond the rushes," Norma said. "You don't have to see one to count it. You can tell by its whistle."

"Its whistle!" Bridgett scoffed. "Listen to you! You can't tell the difference between a call and a song."

"What is the difference?" I asked.

Bridgett said "A call marks territory; a song attracts a mate."

Norma shook her head. "No, I think it's the other way around."

Jacqueline, clearly a romantic, said "I like to think of songbirds as overflowing with such rhapsody, they feel compelled to proclaim their enchantment to the entire world! Wasn't it Keats who wrote,

The lark is so brimful of gladness and love,
The green fields below him, the blue sky above,
That he sings and he sings, and forever sings he,
'I love my love, and my love loves me!'"

Bridgett promptly dashed cold water on this exalted whimsy. "Well you're both wrong," she declared. "Birdsongs simply arise from a biological imperative. Anyway, we've decided upon a new rule. We're only going to count birds that have been visually spotted by at least two observers."

Norma harrumphed. "I'll count any bird I see and whatever song I hear. I have an excellent ear."

Standing next to me, Norma showed me her card: nuthatch, fly snatcher, puffin, snipe, titmouse, reedbird, stoned curlew, scarlet teenager, toucan, bobolink, harpy, kookaburra, and the freshly-added red-winged thistle cropper. "Of course, not all of these sightings were around here. I've traveled a fair amount. These people are Philistines." Then she stomped off through the reeds.

Jacqueline leaned toward me. "Norma's always marking up her card with exotic species no one else has ever seen. Some of them don't even migrate through North America! She claims to have such a keen ear, but she's really the laughingstock of the entire Ornithological Society." She gave an authoritative nod, then quickened her pace to catch up with Bridgett.

"Oh goodness!" she cried, tugging Bridgett's sleeve, "A gaggle of geese!" We all looked up, as high above us, a perfect V of some twenty geese arched across the sky.

"That's not a gaggle, it's a skein," Bridgett said, breaking the silence. "A gaggle's on the water; a skein is in the sky."

"Well whatever you call them," Jacqueline said, "aren't they magnificent?"

Reilly was still gazing skyward. "I've never seen such an exquisite V," he exclaimed. Despite Bridgett's attempt to quell her enthusiasm, Jacqueline beamed at her discovery.

As we continued along the shore, I asked Jacqueline if they'd ever gone birding at night.

"Oh, yes, we've gone night-birding—owls and bats come out, though you can't see too well, since it's dark."

Bridgett overheard her remark, and turned on her with disdain. "Bats are not birds, you ninny. They're mammals."

Jacqueline said, "I know that, but he asked if we went birding at night, and even though they're not birds, that's when we saw them, didn't we?" She looked to Reilly for confirmation.

Reilly cleared his throat. "The Bible erroneously classifies bats as birds; it's in Leviticus. A bat's the sort of bird you're not supposed to eat."

Bridgett said "I would never even think of eating a bat. It's just a rat, with wings!"

Jacqueline said "Well, I wouldn't eat a bat, even if it was a bird."

"Bats and birds!" Bridgett growled, suddenly bored with the entire subject. "You couldn't tell a grackle from a grebe."

Jacqueline looked understandably wounded by this attack. "I can so," she protested. "They come from entirely different families. A grackle's a blackbird; a grebe is a diving—"

Bridget cut her off. "Or a dodo from a booby," she needled.

Sideswiped by this jibe, Jacqueline seemed flustered. "Dodos are extinct!"

"Oh my stars! Who let the cat out of the bag?"

Finally, stung by her sarcasm and fed up with her cruel derision, Jacqueline said "You're the booby."

Bridgett shot back: "You're the dodo."

"Booby-brain!"

"Dodo-head!"

Just then, Reilly piped up:

"I spy—a crimson-crested boobyhatch!"

A Funny Thing Happened on My Way to the Forum

On my way to the Forum, I realized that I was ignorant; then, in the next instant—after getting how stupid I was—I got it that I was a *Totally Enlightened Being*! It was so stupendously, inanely simplistic, I could hardly believe it. All the schooling, all the degrees fell away from me, and I was enthralled by the suchness and thusness of it all. I saw everything revealed exactly the way it was! In that moment, I got that I'm already perfect, just the way I am.

This breakthrough opened up a new spectrum of infinite possibilities. Each and every day, it makes the way I am within myself better and better in every way! Now I see that a commitment exists to fulfill the ultimate potential of what life can be on this planet, here and now in this universe, the way it's constructed in this moment, fulfilling what you are committed to, right now; finding the yes after the no. It's what gets me up in the morning, to share what you share.

Let's take the challenge to step boldly beyond our limited vision of reality—beyond our most cherished assumptions of who we thought we were. We can synergistically access a whole new dimension of being! Aim your focus on living, not knowing. Because what you know has nothing to do with the way you live. In the end, it's what you don't know, and don't know that you don't know, you know?

Are You Normal? A Self-Assessment Guide

1. Do you wake up in the morning and say, "Oh God, I can't face another day."?
2. Are you burdened by the niggling details of everyday life—yet you're perfectly capable of rising to the occasion in the face of a real calamity?
3. Do you brood on revenge fantasies for imagined slights and provocations?
4. Do you dream in color?
5. What's your favorite cookie?

Answers:

1. This is normal.
2. You are more powerful than you think.
3. Everyone does this.
4. You are a very sensual person.
5. Chocolate chip with walnuts.

Supreme Court Allows Gays in the Military

WASHINGTON, D.C.: The Supreme Court ruled today that gays shall be allowed to serve in the military, ending an institutionalized form of discrimination that's lasted for over seventy years. "There really is no basis for this continued bias, other than the prejudiced views of a few ignorant individuals," the Chief Justice wrote in her majority opinion. "Gays and lesbians have served honorably for years, without any of the disruptions previously feared.

"Homophobic attacks against uniformed service personnel will no longer be tolerated," she continued. "The armed forces must deal firmly with such cases, just as they're expected to combat racial and sexual harassment. By putting a stop to the 'Don't ask, don't tell' policy, an era of intimidation, secrecy, and lies will finally be brought to a close."

Cheered by gay rights groups, the decision did not sit well with the military brass, who were tight-lipped and obviously agitated, but not overtly defiant. One of the Chiefs of Staff, who preferred to remain anonymous, said there was no way he'd ever bend over in the shower again for a bar of soap. He ordered soap dispensers for military showers across the land.

The Religious Right, of course, got on their big horn and blew a gasket, claiming the only army in the world that let gays serve in the military was Sodom and Gomorrah, conveniently leaving out Israel and most of the European Community, to say nothing of Sparta's Army of Lovers.

Staff Sergeant Steven Harrington, a plaintiff in the case that made it all the way to the Supreme Court, expressed relief at the decision. "Interestingly, gays in the military tend to be a rather conservative lot, not especially given to public displays of affection; we're more apt to keep our personal lives pretty much to ourselves. We obey orders, do our job, respect other people, and quietly go about our business, just like any good soldier. You don't see a lot of parading around with whips and chains, cavorting in G-strings, or dancing to a disco beat in many of the military training camps around the country."

Asked if he thought that would change, now that gays could serve openly, Harrington said "I don't think so. Giggling and camping it up are just not that common in the armed forces, and I don't think there's going to be a big change along those lines. Although I've heard about the drag shows during World War II that sounded like a hoot and a half, but that was during a pretty stressful time of war. Everybody's got to blow off a little steam some time."

What about the concerns of heterosexual men that gays might try to take advantage of them?

"All these straight guys afraid some gay soldier is gonna peek at their wiener in the shower can just get over themselves. There's nothing more boring than a straight man just lying there while you do all the work. They're way too uptight—gay guys like moaning and groaning when we're making love. A little hugging and smooching, gazing into each other's eyes, caressin' and lovin'.

"Who wants to give someone head who just sits there stiff as a board, terrified he might be a faggot just 'cause he let some guy suck him off? First he gets a blow job, then instead of expressing gratitude, he pounds the shit out of the guy who blew him.

"You think that's all we want? In a pinch, if you're really horny, sure; but we like a little reciprocation, just like anybody else. Honestly, we've got better things to do with our time than lust after straight guys. The pay-off is just not that gratifying."

Was Jesus Bipolar?

New York: The *Journal for the Psychoanalytic Study of Religion* released a study today that strongly suggests Jesus suffered from a bipolar disorder. This announcement set loose a paroxysm of pandemonium among the religious establishment, the usual denials and denunciations, but it makes you kind of wonder—what if he was?

Have you ever thought you might be manic-depressive? You wake up with megatons of energy, you're on top of the world, your mind races along at ninety miles an hour. You stay up all night like you're on speed for days at a time and you're totally flying—I'm a bird, I'm a plane, I'm superman! You have great insights, you're inspired, completely confident you can accomplish miracles! You spend money like it's going out of style, you don't have a worry in the world—totally maxing on self-confidence. You tell everyone you'll be rich, famous, the world is your oyster, and you're the pearl!

Then you crash—the next day is like the worst hangover in history. The world is dark, it sucks, it's bad, it's utterly odious, repulsive, ghastly, and abhorrent. All the fantastic insights from the week before seem like a fool's paradise, absolutely delusional. You're wracked with doubt, self loathing, and disgust.

Now these psychoanalysts suspect Jesus might have been manic-depressive. Outrageous, sacrilegious, yes, but think about it—Jesus was what—thirty years old, not a clue what to do with his life, totally bummed out, so he goes off to the desert for forty days and forty nights, nothing to eat or drink, he starts hallucinating. One minute he thinks he's the son of God, the next minute he's talking to Satan, who starts egging him on, tempting him to take a flying leap. "Yo! Jesus! Think you're so hot—why doncha just climb to the pinnacle of that temple and dive off? If you're really Christ, God'll swoop down and save you!"

He's tempted to do it, just to show him, but then thinks better of it. "I don't have to prove it." He sneers at Satan, and goes back to town.

Back home, he gets all cocky again. He sweeps into the temple and throws out the money changers. His friends go "Whoa! Dude! Don't mess with the money men!"

"I don't give a fig! They got no business desecrating the temple!"

"Says who!" asks Joe Centurion, the bank's enforcer.

"Says me! The King of the Jews, that's who!" Higher than a kite, Jesus runs around chatting up prostitutes, thumbing his nose at the Pharisees. He's a regular miracle worker, walking on water, exorcising demons, turning water into wine, multiplying bread and fish, healing the blind, raising the dead. He's on a roll.

Trouble is, the Romans don't like upstarts, and even his own people can't wait to get rid of him. Judas gives him the kiss-off, and after Jesus is arrested Peter denies he ever knew him— "Jesus from Nazareth? Maybe I knew a Jesus once, but he was from San Juan."

When Pontius Pilate gives them the choice, even the mob would rather save Barabbas. So they crucify him. Hung up on the cross, Jesus goes into a real downer. "Lord, Lord, why have you forsaken me?"

All his disciples figured: crucified, dead and buried, that's the end of it. But this guy doesn't quit. On the third day, he's back! Thomas doubts the rumors until Jesus waltzes into town, showing off his stigmata.

Now he says anyone who believes he's the Son of God will never die. Just to make sure, he sits at the right hand of God the Father Almighty, from whence he shall judge the quick and the dead.

Talk about delusions of grandeur! Is this guy on a manic high or what? But it can't last forever—sooner or later he's gotta crash. Just wait till he gets the blue meanies again! He'll come riding into town on a white stallion with the four horsemen of the Apocalypse.

I don't want to be there.

Cuban Boy Seeks Asylum in Sweden

MIAMI: Alien Gonzalez, caught in a bitter custody battle between his Miami relatives and his Cuban father, has sought asylum in Sweden. The story, familiar to everyone by now, of the six-year old refugee found floating in an inner tube off the coast of Florida last Thanksgiving, has touched the hearts of millions. Alien soon became embroiled in a tug-of-war that undermined the already strained relations between the two cold war adversaries.

The young Cuban was on an outing with his relatives to Disney World, when he escaped from the Mickey tram and fled to the Swedish consulate. Diane Sawyer, a well-known TV journalist, caught up with Alien, hoping to get a quote from the little boy about his intentions. Away from the influence of his Miami relatives, he was finally able to express his true wishes:

I decided I was being used as a pawn in the cold war squabble between the United States and Cuba. I miss my father and grandmothers terribly, and my Miami relatives have gone out of their way to make me feel welcome. But I really need to look at what sort of life I would be leading if I returned to Cuba, versus staying in the United States.

In Cuba, you can count on equal access to higher education and free medical care, a good job, and a loving family that's not all caught up in consumerism. But, it's a little boring at times, sitting around the old hacienda, guessing how long it's going to take the chicken to cross the road.

Whereas in the United States, you have the freedom to become all that you can be! Only it seems somewhat limited to tawdry displays of conspicuous consumption, with the level of aesthetic taste rarely rising above Mickey Mouse. In short, life in the United States is full of opportunity, but it's really pretty tacky.

So I've decided, I'm out of here. Me and my Papa's family are moving to Sweden, where there's an old-world *savoir-faire*, but with plenty of access to modern technology. There's also an appreciation for some of the finer things in life, without the Wal-Mart mentality that pervades so much of the American ethos. Not to be anti-proletarian, because I really appreciate the solidarity of the laboring classes. Only in Cuba, so much is oriented to glorifying the state, and any individual initiative or vision is suspect: it's commonly criticized as self-indulgent or even counter-revolutionary.

So I bid farewell to my Miami relatives, who were obstinate in their determination that I not be reared in a communist dictatorship. Although I found some of their concern a bit overreaching and self-serving, they gave me a clear picture of what I'd be missing if I went back to Cuba. Frankly, I did not find the prospect of staying in the U.S. terribly tempting.

And I will miss my *abuelitas*, my precious little grandmothers, in Cuba, and my carefree life there, swimming in warm tropical waters, eating coconuts, and working in the sugar cane fields. I continue to support the ideals of the revolution: a classless society with equal opportunity for education, health care, and stable jobs serving the needs of the entire community, not just the demands of capital.

But Cuba has its limitations, too: constantly looking over your shoulder for the local rep from the Committee in Defense of the Revolution, as if any unique thought were a threat to the wider community. It can be a bit stifling at times, especially for an artist with a visionary sensibility. Call it individualistic if you like, but I must follow where my heart leads me.

So farewell to you all: America, with its emphasis on individual responsibility, slave to the demands of capital; and Cuba, socialist utopia, *mi patria*—my home; *mi corazon*—my heart. My newly adopted country awaits me.

Marilyn Monroe Hailed as New First Lady

AFTER A YEAR of mourning following the death of Jackie in the terrible assassination attempt in Dallas last fall, the grief-stricken President has delighted the nation with the announcement that he's taken Marilyn Monroe as his new bride. They were married in a private ceremony over the weekend in Hyannis Port, where brother Bobby served as best man. Teddy drove the newlyweds to the airport, where they held a brief press conference and posed for photographers.

"My philandering days are over," the youthful President said, as Marilyn cooed and whispered a seductive "Happy Birthday, Mr. President" in his ear.

Asked where they met, they exchanged glances, then Mr. Kennedy said, "At a fox hunt."

"Yes, that was it," Marilyn agreed. "A fox hunt. Only they never caught the fox, did they?" She batted her enormous eyelashes at the President, who blushed.

As the First Lady, what duties or interests do you plan to pursue?

"Well I'd like to continue redecorating the White House," she said, referring to Jackie's famous attempts to update its aging decor. "And I'd like to be a good mother to Jack's children."

What about your film career? Are your acting days over?

"I'd love to serve as a liaison to the film industry, to enhance the cultural life of the United States. And I'd still like to entertain our troops abroad, to keep up their morale. But I think at least for now, I'll have to forgo the lure of the silver screen."

When contacted for comment, former husband Joe DiMaggio was tight-lipped. "I only wish her the best," Joe said. "She always batted 1000 in my league."

Arthur Miller agreed. "She always liked the spotlight—well now she's got it, big time. It's the greatest role she'll ever get."

Movie moguls were ecstatic. "We can't wait for her next picture," a spokesperson said. "She says she's too busy for the movies, now, but we know Marilyn. She'll be back. We thought we'd cast her as Cleopatra, in *Queen of the Nile*. How could she resist? Art imitates life."

Even before Air Force One whisked the happy couple away on their honeymoon, portraits and calendars of Marilyn had sprung up on the walls of offices, factories, gas stations, garages, barracks, gym lockers, and restrooms across the land, which demonstrates the fondness and high esteem with which our new First Lady is regarded by an adoring public.

Women began imitating her inimitable style, shunning the pillbox hats and helmet hairdo of her predecessor: now they bleached their hair and wore white mink stoles with ropes of diamonds and pearls. Strangely, in the weeks that followed, scores of women found themselves caught over windy grates! They all struggled as best they could to keep their skirts from blowing up around them.

Midnight Rambler

MY MOTHER was famous for her bouts of insomnia, which lasted sometimes until daybreak. After tossing half the night, she'd finally forsake any chance of further slumber and get up to do something "useful."

My father decried her midnight rambles, as he called them. He claimed her usefulness consisted in lying next to him, warding off the chill of encroaching darkness through long stretches of winter somnolence.

"Poppycock," my mother said. She shoved a bolster beneath the blanket whenever she arose, deep in the night, to tend to her nocturnal chores. Long after I'd gone to bed, I could hear the rhythmic sounds of her kneading dough or scrubbing the kitchen floor.

My father seemed not to notice her absence, as he'd comment the next morning on her stolidness in bed the previous night. "Sleeping soundly, are we?"

"As sound as the deepening well," she replied. My father wrinkled his brow, as he seemed to find her response oddly unsettling.

Late one night, I got up for a glass of water and found her rocking in the living room, gazing at the moon rising past the chimney of the house next door. "Mama," I said, "what are you doing?"

Her face shone in the moonlight as she drew me close, caressing my cheek with her warm hand. "I'm communing," she said. I climbed into her lap and she wrapped me in her quilt, rocking and humming softly, stroking my hair.

After a while she kissed my forehead. "Run along now, and go to sleep."

On summery moonlit nights, I'd hear the click of the front door as I lay in bed, the scent of jasmine drifting through my window. Rising on my knees, I'd lean on the sill and watch her take long strides toward the river. Even during the day, my father objected to her strolling along the embankment, but she said the sound of the black current rushing by the willows soothed her.

Only once did I dare follow along. I pulled my robe over my pajamas and slipped into the darkness. When I caught up with her by the riverbank, she did not scold me. She held me between her knees as we huddled in the dank grass under the willow, watching the branches skip and bounce against the silky torrent. Tiny waves flashed in the moonlight like the fins of silvery fish flying just beneath the surface.

One night, she'd locked herself out. She came around to the kitchen to try the screen door, but it was latched. Not wanting to wake the whole house, she went out back and shinnied up the drain pipe to reach the dining room window, six feet off the ground. As she raised the sash, it screeched and rattled against the frame, rousing my father from his sound repose.

"What's that?" he said, sitting up. He felt for my mother, but the bolster was unresponsive. Assuming she was asleep, he got out of bed and took his shotgun from the closet. He tiptoed down the hallway and silently swung open the door to the dining room. Crouched in his nightshirt, he squinted at the dim figure of my mother, jack-knifed over the window sill. The window jiggled loose, trapping her lightly but firmly at the waist. "Umf," she said.

Thrusting his gun like a bayonet, my father lunged into the room. "Who is it, who is it, who is it!"

My mother arched her back, lifting her arms in the darkness. "It's me, it's me, it's me!" she wailed, bobbing in mid-air.

My father stopped, confused in the rush of his sudden wakefulness. "It can't be you," he said. "You're asleep, in bed."

"No I'm not!" she insisted. "I couldn't sleep, so I took a walk." She reached toward him, wriggling her fingers. "Pull me through!"

My father cocked his head, peering at her suspiciously. Doubled over the sill, her voice sounded crimped and strange. He withdrew to the hallway and returned to the bedroom. "Millie?" he called. He leaned over to shake the bolster by the foot. Alarmed by its silence, he flung back the covers. "She's gone!"

Meanwhile, I'd wandered into the dining room to see what all the ruckus was about. Mother pushed on the baseboard while flailing her legs against the outside wall. The curtains billowed in the moonlight as she stretched her hand toward a chair to pull herself in.

"Mama?"

"Honey," she said, "come here. See if you can lift the window."

Too short to reach the top of the frame, I tried the bottom. Since I was only able to lift one side, the sash tilted and stuck.

My father entered from the hallway, the shotgun still in his hand. I turned to face him. "Daddy, don't shoot! It's only Mama."

"For crying out loud," he said. He came over and jammed the gun barrel under the sash to jimmy the window. Suddenly, the gun went off with a terrific burst that rattled the house. The explosion left us stunned for a moment, as the enormity of what might have happened sunk in.

"Mama!" I cried, and rushed to her side.

My father lay the gun on the floor and knelt beside her. "Millie! Are you all right?"

"Good heavens!" she said. "I think so." She cocked her head to one side. "I just seem to be a little deaf."

He lifted her off the sill and she sat in a heap on the floor, her legs folded beneath her. She was shaken, but uninjured. In the morning we would discover the blast had demolished my father's favorite rose bush just outside the window, a prize-winning *Pink Peace*.

Mama swept a lock of hair from her face and tucked it under her barrette. "I forgot my key."

My father shook his head. "You've left me nigh a widower to your restless jaunts!" He sounded exasperated, yet relieved. Then he picked up his gun and retreated down the hall.

Mama stood up, brushing her housecoat, and bent down to kiss my cheek. I clutched her legs, suddenly overwhelmed.

"What's this, now?"

I couldn't say anything.

She gently pried my fingers loose. "Come along, dear, let's go to bed. We've had enough excitement for one night." She took me by the hand and led me back to my room. I scooted beneath the covers and she tucked me in.

"Don't pay any mind to all this commotion," she said. "Sometimes we get a little restless, is all."

Backlit by the overhead lamp, her hair framed her face like a golden halo. A lock came loose from the barrette and fell along the nape of her neck. I reached out to twirl the strands of hair around my finger.

"Now close those eyes and go to sleep." She stroked my forehead and kissed my eyelids. "You don't want to take after your mama, do you?"

She got up to leave, and I could still feel the warmth of her hand alongside my cheek. I propped myself on my elbow, not wanting to let her out of my sight.

She turned when she reached the doorway. "Go on now, sweetheart, lie down and get some rest." She blew me a kiss, then shut off the light and closed the door.

Falling back against the pillow, I listened to her footsteps pad down the hall. I crossed my arms behind my head and squeezed my eyes tight, but sleep had left me. I lay still in the darkness, and watched the moon as it rose on its nightly journey past the chimney next door.

Man Claims Car Accident Made Him Gay

Iowa City: A man has successfully sued for damages following a car accident that he claims turned him into a homosexual.

Frank Kopotnik, 44, was side-swiped in a crash last October. Following a hospital stay of two weeks, he inexplicably fell out of love with his wife. Not only had he lost all sexual interest in her, but he could no longer imagine having sexual relations with any woman. In fact, his libidinous desire had turned exclusively toward men. With his life in a shambles following a messy divorce, he fell in love with his best friend, who spurned him. That's when he decided to sue.

Doctors were puzzled by this phenomenon. "We've never seen anything like it," they said. "This case suggests a causative link between physical trauma and sex-object desire. We don't really understand what mechanism might be at work here. It is quite enigmatic."

Gay rights groups were also perplexed. Because of our homophobic culture, it commonly takes a while for a young person to get in touch with same-sex desire, but gays commonly insist that nothing "made" them that way. While they welcomed a new member of their tribe, they weren't sure that becoming gay should be a cause for litigation, since it suggested there was something unseemly about being attracted to the same sex.

"I don't have anything against gay people," Kopotnik said. "I just did not happen to be one, and to suddenly become gay has been incredibly disruptive to my lifestyle. It's not something I would have chosen, and it has caused untold difficulties for myself and my family, as you can imagine. I believe I deserve some compensation for the problems I've suffered as a consequence."

Some skeptics suspect Kopotnik is using the accident as an excuse to come out of the closet, denying he had any choice in the matter; and while you're at it, why not make a bundle?

Mr. Kopotnik disputes this claim. "I never had any sexual desire for men before the accident. At the hospital, I had a male nurse who sucked me off each night before I went to sleep, and I admit I found that a pleasurable experience, but I certainly had no intention of becoming gay because of it. Yet once I got out of the hospital, I went looking for dick wherever I could find it. The only thing I can figure is that the accident joggled something inside my brain—it crossed my synapses or something, and that's what made me gay."

Asked whether he couldn't simply refrain from indulging his impulses, he shook his head. "No, I don't think that would be the right way to go. Sure, I could just pretend that I'm not really gay, but that would only add more confusion to the pain and trauma I've already suffered."

What about seeking some sort of treatment, like reparative therapy, so you can return to heterosexuality?

"I wish I was still straight, but alas, I'm not. It's not like I really have any choice in the matter. As much as I'd like to change back, everyone knows those treatments never work. I simply have to accept the fact that I'm gay, and move on with my life. Now I want dick, and by God, I'm going to have it."

The jury awarded Mr. Kopotnik fifty million dollars to compensate for the humiliation, pain, and suffering brought about by this remarkable shift in his sexual orientation.

Jesus Withers Fig Tree with Scorn

BETHANY: Jesus and his disciples stopped by a fig tree on their way to Jerusalem to refresh themselves with its fruit. Unfortunately, it wasn't in season, so there weren't any figs. Jesus was peeved, and scorned the tree: "May no man eat fruit of thee hereafter for ever."

(The same day he cursed the fig, he threw the money-changers out of the Temple, so he must have been having one of his moods.)

The next day, on their way back to Bethany, Peter noticed the shriveled tree, and said "Look! The fig tree which you cursed has withered."

Jesus said "Have faith in God. Truly, I say to you, whoever says to this mountain, 'Be taken up and cast into the sea,' and does not doubt in his heart, but believes that what he says will come to pass, it will be done for him. Therefore I tell you, whatever you ask in prayer, believe that you receive it, and you will."

Now, this is a pretty amazing claim! Not only that God would grant any prayer, as long as you have faith; but that He would respond to such an arbitrary curse—it makes one shudder.

Did Jesus seriously believe the tree was being willful by withholding its figs, and thus deserving of his scorn and punishment? If you won't satisfy us now, you shall be condemned for your inhospitable treatment of ravenous travelers, and you shall cease satisfying anyone, ever again. In fact, thou shalt wither and die.

What a sense of entitlement—to say nothing of spite! It doesn't matter that it's not fig season, I want my figs now! And if I can't have my figs this instant, no one shall have them, ever. Furthermore, you will perish for not bearing figs when I happen to pass by—never mind that I came this way when no fig is on any tree, anywhere. I am here, now; I am in need of refreshment; therefore, you should have anticipated my privation and produced figs, even in the depths of winter.

If Jesus had the power to wither a tree merely by scorning it, couldn't he have coaxed it to produce figs out of season? After all, he changed water into wine. One can't help but surmise Jesus was having a bad day—even the Lord can be irascible.

Do Cats Purr on Purpose?

Do cats purr with conscious calculation? If a cat is perfectly content, but no human is around to observe, does she still purr? I wonder if lions, tigers, cheetahs, jaguars, leopards, or panthers purr, perhaps after a spectacularly satisfying kill, or when licking their cubs.

The domestic cat meows to get us to do her bidding, like feeding her or letting her outside, where she howls and hisses at the neighbor's tom. But to what purpose does she purr?

Does she purr to seduce us, or to demonstrate her pleasure? Maybe purring is essentially involuntary: cats purr simply from a sense of delicious contentment with the world, and there's no intention involved at all—purring is like a baby's smile, all innocence and mirth.

Cats purr when you stroke them, hold them on your lap, and even when you tickle their tummy—funny how they keep purring even as they dig their claws into your flesh and bite your thumb, shaking it like a mouse, but then you probably had it coming.

They say when cats rub up against you, even if they're purring, it's not because they're being affectionate, they're merely marking territory with their musky oils. What seems so endearingly affectionate to us is simply a way of making us off-limits to other cats. Humans often mistake possessiveness as a sign of devotion, heedless of its sinister dangers, so it's no surprise we're taken in by wily felines.

I asked my cat, Delia, if she purrs simply from serene contentment, to express affection, or as a means of influencing my behavior?

She sniffed the air, the tip of her tail bent, as she nimbly walked across the top of the couch, apparently ignoring my query. But then she turned to me, and said "Cats are utterly guileless. We live in the moment; there's not a lick of calculation. We do not purr in order to gain anything; we have no concept of intention. If we purr, it is because we are content—that is all."

Suspecting her explanation was a tad disingenuous, I pressed further. "So do you purr when I'm not around?"

Sensing my skepticism, she wrinkled her nose, as if this were an unseemly question. "I'm not certain where this line of inquiry is leading," she said.

I should have realized she was leery of some legalistic entrapment, but I blundered ahead with my naïve curiosity. "Like when you and Missy are home alone, batting a ball of yarn, torturing a mouse, or sitting on the window sill staring out at the world, do you purr in contentment then?"

She turned around and nimbly walked away from me, her tail twitching. It was obvious that I'd stumbled on a rather delicate area she didn't want to pursue. She would never admit her purring had anything to do with expressing affection, seducing me, or influencing my behavior.

I had another question—what about her antic capers, dashing from one room to the other, her eyes wild, chasing a dustball? Was her purr during such a frenzied frolic ecstatic, or simply agitated? But she had said her piece, and that was the end of it.

As a matter of fact, ever since I brought this matter up, she hasn't purred (or otherwise spoken to me) since. Sure, she'll tolerate me lifting her onto my lap and petting her once or twice, stroking her chin, but then she'll spring to the floor and walk away with complete indifference. Even when I'm opening a can of tuna, rather than skittering between my legs and purring up a storm, she now waits quite patiently, and then eats out of her dish with dignity, without a whisper of a purr. I used to comment on her anticipated pleasure: "Yum! Dinner time! That gets your motor going, doesn't it!" But alas, no more. Even Missy has been a little stand-offish of late, influenced no doubt by her sister.

I suspect I've violated some feline rule, which forbids anticipation—whatever sign of affection she deigns to offer should be graciously accepted when it's gratuitously granted, and never expected. The slightest hint of obligation will be met with utter disdain. Whether it's intentional or not, I'm essentially powerless over whether my puss will purr, and I should simply accept that such a gift is granted or withheld entirely at her pleasure.

Stop Scoffing at Marriage!

NOWADAYS, you can hardly open a magazine, turn on the radio or TV without being affronted with an assault on matrimony. We live in a time when mortal sin is dismissed as a mere peccadillo. Cuckolded husbands are treated with amusement, their wives winked at for their brash adultery. The President gets away with unbridled passion, with nary a repercussion to his reputation. On the contrary, he is cheered on by the brutish herd! Even homosexuals feel free to mock this cherished institution by claiming marriage rights for themselves.

With temptation lurking all around us, the last thing we need is a reminder of base, bestial urges! The seductive wink, the wiggling tush, the low moan or wolfish whistle have no place in civilized society! These seductive signals all demean God's plan for a chaste and happy marriage! And they distract one from the path of true faithfulness. Even if there's no carnal contact, burning with lustful desire is still adultery! Indulging in impure thoughts offends the righteous, and makes the angels weep.

What is to be done, lest our culture degenerate into a howling pit of decadent degradation? We must rescue marriage from the cesspool of sexual innuendo! True matrimonial bliss is not furthered by lewd depictions of lust and lasciviousness. Let's ban sensual advertisements, that flaunt the flesh in unseemly displays of pornographic licentiousness! In their place, let us present charming depictions of virtuous wives and faithful husbands, sitting by the fireside: Goody goodwife in her becoming bonnet, darning socks by candlelight, while her husband, Increase, scours the *Financial Times*, or bounces a towhead on his knee.

It's time for the scrupulous majority to remake the moral landscape of this great nation. Don't give in to temptation, sloth, and heedless mirth! Stiffen your moral backbone! Make demands! Call on your pastor, your children's teachers and principals, yea, even your representatives in the halls of Congress, to take action against the moral turpitude of this collapsing culture!

Make it personal! Take offense to demeaning remarks about matrimony, even if others appear to enjoy them. In all likelihood, they are simply covering their embarrassment with a chuckle, and they will welcome your intercession. If you hear a wisecrack about the "old ball and chain," don't just stand idly by the water cooler while fellow workers ridicule and scorn this noble institution. You must speak up! "How dast thou cast aspersion on the sacrosanct sacrament of marriage!" Your coworkers will be cowed in shame.

You'll be amazed at the respect you will gain when you forthrightly take such a brave stand. They'll say, "There walks an upright man, if ever I saw one!"

Come, let us join together in a universal appeal to good citizens to uphold, protect, and defend the very basis of Christian civilization: Stay the course of righteousness! Harness the yoke of matrimony! Screw tight the shackles of wedlock! Stop scoffing at marriage!

The Folly of Irrational Exuberance

QUENTIN FOX, dot com entrepreneur and best-selling author of *The Tao of Dow*, has recently exhibited signs of considerable enthusiasm, especially since his stock has split nine times in the past year, even though his company has yet to fill a single order of widgets.

When asked whether he thought his exuberance might be a tad irrational, Mr. Fox denied the charge. "We're quite sanguine about the future," he assured this reporter while dancing a jig. "As a matter of fact, we are absolutely ecstatic!" He leapt in the air in a double twist, letting out a high-pitched squeal before composing himself again.

Asked whether his bottom line justified the stock market's interest in widgets, he pooh-poohed the question. "How many start-ups fail to make a profit in their first year? We need capital investment, but more than that, we need vision!" He did a somersault, then sprang to his feet.

Dismissing his critics, he said "What fraidy cats they are, cowering behind their dour prognostications, growling their bearish pessimism! Don't they realize the future is open! It's wide! It's possible, plausible, and probable! A telecosmic opportunity, just waiting to be tapped!" Here he did a few shuffles in a fair approximation of the old soft shoe.

But shouldn't stock prices have some relation to earnings?

"That's old, that's past, that's lag-behind, pessimistic Pooh-Bah! Widgetry is gadgetry, it exists on the physical plane only so long as it serves the metaphysical triumph of capital! What you have here is a quantum leap beyond the paradigm of foggy, fear-based cogitation!"

Mr. Fox shoved his palms alternately in front of him while executing a slick set of Charleston kicks. "I take, I give, I metamorphize the moment!" Then he clicked his heels. "Exchange is elasticity, movement is life!" He did a back-flip, his horn-rimmed glasses sliding to the end of his nose. This, plus the rumpled appearance of his cheap black suit and stringy tie gave him an odd, Ichabod Crane sort of look, despite his reputed wealth and obvious dexterity.

"Geek geek geek!" he suddenly exclaimed, crouching like a quarterback. (I admit this characterization had occurred to me as well, but I was too polite to say so.) Then he yelled "Geek on the loose! Geek's got the goose!" and charged ahead, knocking this reporter on his butt. "We were the loner stoners, not the loser boozers, but guess who got the golden egg!" He held the imaginary egg aloft. "So who's got egg on their faces, now? That's right, all those soshes, the popular kids who partied on down, but got left behind in the dustbin of history!"

He then tried to sign me up for a multi-level marketing plan to distribute widgets world-wide. "You want to get in on the bottom rung of the top floor! This is not just dungeons and dragons, my little laddy-boy. This is top-flight, top-drawer, instantaneous streams of fortune!" He puffed out his cheeks and wiggled his nose in what appeared to be an imitation of a chipmunk, then hung his hands in front of him and hopped about like a kangaroo.

"Imagine yourself at the top of a pyramid, while far below your base grows exponentially into the bottomless future." He opened his arms wide, then twirled in a lovely pirouette. "You get a portion of the profit of every sale of every widget beneath you for eternity! All you have to do is say 'yes' to now! Is that so hard to do?" He took a flying leap, his arms outstretched, and landed on toe.

He fixed me with a piercing look. "*You show the still, calm style of a sleuth seeking insight and proof!*" he declared, obviously trying to con me with a line from some corny musical. For a small investment equal to the down-payment of a luxury car, he offered to sign me up on the spot, my cache of widgets to arrive in the near future, along with complete instructions for farming out my ever-expanding base of widgetry, plus inspirational tapes by yours truly. "And, to make this enticing offer something you cannot possibly resist and still consider yourself a sane person, I'm throwing in my aerobic exercise DVD!"

Though I'm sure he considered this latest gambit the absolute clincher, I wasn't terribly tempted. "Don't lose out!" he cried. Then he careered through several cartwheels in a circle, shouting "Look at me! Look at me! Look at me!"

Vision-impaired as I was (and feeling a little dizzy), I politely declined the opportunity.

Widget stock has since split again, and continues to climb.

Can Dogs Be Bad?

YOU FREQUENTLY hear people say "good dog" or "bad dog" to discipline their pets, but can dogs really be bad? Sure, they might not do what you want and look guilty as sin, but do they really have a conscience? I wonder.

After a particularly boisterous episode, when Biff had chewed my slipper, tipped over the birdcage, and zoomed through the house with a roll of toilet paper trailing behind him, I sat him down for a serious talk.

"Bad dog! Bad dog!" I scolded. Biff hung his head. "Look at what you've done!" I pointed at the trail of mayhem he'd left in his wake. He whined a little and stretched out his front legs. "What in the world were you thinking?" He crept closer, and laid his head on my foot. "You're a bad, bad dog!" He put his paws over his muzzle and tried to hide his eyes. "I just don't understand what's gotten into you!" He uncovered one adorable eye to peek up at me, then licked my big toe.

Now, an impartial observer might conclude that these acts of contrition betray a guilty conscience—so he *knows* he was bad. Or are these submissive gestures designed to placate and seduce his agitated master, the ostensible alpha male? He "knows" he's not supposed to knock over the bird cage and tear through the house with a roll of toilet paper trailing behind him, jump on the furniture with soiled paws, or drink out of the toilet—yet he does it anyway. Why? Inquiring minds want to know.

Randy, my seven-year old nephew, offered a plausible theory. "I know why Biff's bad," he said.

"Oh, why's that?"

"Because it's fun, that's why."

"But does he really know that he's being bad?"

"Oh, yes. He knows what he's not supposed to do. But if no one's around to tell him not to, he'll go ahead and do it anyway."

I thought this was a very likely explanation for Randy's behavior, who plunges into mischief as soon as you turn your back, but I wasn't sure if it really described Biff's own internal process.

I turned back to my dog, who now sat obediently at my feet. "Biff, Biff, why do you always chew my slippers, when time and again I've told you not to?"

Imagine my astonishment when Biff responded to my query!

"It's because they're so musty and smelly," he admitted. "They're all leathery and chewy and raggedy and munchable."

"But don't you know by now that you're not supposed to?"

"I know you'll get mad if I do it."

"So why do you persist?"

"I cannot resist temptation."

"In the act of deciding to chew or not to chew, does the thought even occur to you: 'This is bad'?"

"Only after the fact, when you get mad. If I thought about it for a second, yes, I might be able to register the notion: *chewing slipper* equals *bad dog*. But in the moment, when confronted by an unguarded slipper, I'm much too excited to recall that it's bad. I don't even think twice, I simply snatch and chew."

"Well, could you kindly explain why it is that some dogs can be taught to control their impulses and not chew daddy's favorite slipper?"

Biff pondered this question with a distracted, dreamy expression for a long while, although whether he was actually considering it, or was merely contemplating the tantalizing rapture of munching again on my musty slipper, I'm not entirely clear.

"Maybe it's because I'm a Jack Russell terrier?" he ventured.

The vet diagnosed him with ADADD: *Adult Dog Attention Deficit Disorder*, and put him on Ritalin. Ever since then he has stopped chewing on my slippers. What a miracle! When I come home from work, instead of barking like a maniac, springing in the air, twirling around three times, and leaping onto every piece of furniture in a mad dash around the room, now he greets me at the door, takes my hat and coat, hands me the evening paper, brings me my pipe and slippers, and serves me an icy tumbler of Jack Daniel's.

"Good dog!"

Sin Peddlers

THE REVEREND WILLY SHAG called a press conference today to denounce the endorsement of "sin peddlers" by the Travel section of the Sunday *Times*. He held high a copy of the offending paper in one hand, while wagging his finger at the press corps with the other.

"This scurrilous filth has got to stop!" he said, his face red, spittle flying from his mouth. "It's one thing to have porn on the internet, flooding our movie houses, and destroying family entertainment on TV—but have we stooped so low that you advertise the peddling of sin at resorts in the Sunday Travel section?"

He held up the newspaper and quoted the scandalous review of an isolated resort on the Yucatan peninsula: " 'What's important is that there's an impeccable white beach (*sin* peddlers), palm trees aplenty, tepid azure waters and an endless supply of *muy fuerte* margaritas.'

"What are we to make of this? You're now encouraging families to take their kids to beaches where they brazenly peddle *sin*? One can only imagine the deviant escapades offered for sale at such a decadent resort! No doubt, the usual panoply of drugs, perversion, wholesale whoredom, homosexual slave boys, and bestiality! You might expect to find such filth in the bars of Tijuana, hussies and harlots offering themselves to donkeys to entertain drunken sailors from San Diego, but at a family resort? And right on the beach! This is barbarous!

"And you call yourselves a family newspaper! I am calling for a boycott of your paper, your advertisers, and of any travel agency that books flights to this godforsaken hell-hole!"

Having read the article myself, I could see the mistake that the good Reverend had fallen into, so I decided to take a stab at correcting his error. "Reverend, I suspect you're the unwitting victim of a linguistic misapprehension."

"What's that?" He peered at me suspiciously, shading his eyes with the newspaper.

"The word *sin* in the article is actually the Spanish word for 'without.'"

"Without sin?"

"Not without sin, exactly, but without peddlers."

"But what about sin!"

I suspected my argument was getting derailed, so I tried another angle. "You see, the point the author was making was that you can walk along this pristine beach without being hassled by peddlers offering you souvenirs: '*sin* peddlers' means 'without peddlers,' like you often find at nearby popular resorts such as Cancun or Cozumel."

The Reverend shook his head, and jabbed the paper with his forefinger. "They even put it in italics, to emphasize that's the very point they're making! It's right there if you'd bother to read it: '*sin* peddlers'!"

"Well, it's true that italics are sometimes used to provide emphasis, as you say, but writers also use italics to designate a foreign word—like a little further down, they use italics with the phrase *muy fuerte* Margaritas. That's Spanish for a 'very strong' Margarita."

He looked at me suspiciously, but I forged ahead. "The word *sin* is Spanish for 'without,' so the phrase '*sin* peddlers' doesn't mean they're peddling sin; it means 'without any peddlers.' You can walk down the beach without being bothered by anyone trying to sell you anything. Including sin. You see what I'm saying?"

"Are you playing me for a fool?" he demanded, the color rising on his neck.

"No, I'm not! Look, here's a Spanish-English dictionary." I had brought one along, anticipating the opportunity to counter this simple misreading. I stepped up to the podium and showed him the page. "See, it's right here: *sin* in Spanish means 'without.'"

"Are you telling me there's no sin in Spanish?"

"Of course there is." I flipped to the English-Spanish side: "Sin in Spanish is *pecado*, you see; it's a completely different word."

"Now you say *pecado* means sin! But you just said *sin* means 'without!' I took logic in college, my friend, so don't take me for some kind of ninny. If A=B, and B=C, then A=C. Therefore, *pecado* means 'without,' and we're still left with *sin*!"

I took a deep breath and tried it again. "The Spanish word, *sin*, means 'without.' But the English meaning of sin is expressed in Spanish by the word *pecado*." The Reverend narrowed his eyes, and I rapidly continued. "So the writer wasn't talking about 'sin' at all. He was just trying to be clever, using the Spanish word for 'without' to indicate you could walk down the beach without being hassled by peddlers."

He looked at me as though he couldn't quite tell whether I was trying to pull the wool over his eyes. "You're saying this reporter was just being cutesy with his Spanish to show how carefree you could walk down the beach without getting hustled?"

"Exactly!" I said, nodding my head and grinning like a fool, proud of my ability to clarify this needless misunderstanding. Lord knows we have enough real conflicts in this world without confounding them with misperceptions.

But the Reverend turned on me with a vengeance. "You can explain all you want how the Spanish means this and the Spanish means that, but right here in black and white is what I'm talking about, and it says clear as day that if you go to this beach, you're unquestionably going to be peddled *sin*!"

I tried to object, but he put up his hand. "You just don't realize how clever this reporter was being, that's all. He knew *precisely* what he was doing—yeah, yeah, maybe in Spanish he implies you can walk around without getting hassled, but who remembers their high school Spanish? He cleverly inserts an intentional innuendo of ambiguity because he knows full well that you'll understand his real meaning, 'cause he spells it right out in so many words: '*sin* peddlers.' Yes!" he insisted, as I shook my head.

"So if you don't want to be bothered with trinkets, that's all fine and dandy, but if it's *sin* you're looking for, this is just the place you're going to find it! Ha ha! Got you there, bud, don't think you can pull my leg, I've been around the block a few times, I can detect a smart subterfuge when it's standing right in front of your eyes, plain as day—step right up, fly to Mexico, get your *sin* peddlers right on the beach! Case closed."

At this point I retreated, chastened by the unyielding power of a fixed idea.

Patents Granted for Designer Genes

BEVERLY HILLS: Following the completion of the Human Genome Project, a mad scramble has taken place for the licensing of our beauty genes.

Genie, Inc., the new start-up for genetic applications, has cornered the market with patents for an enticing array of designer genes, such as high cheek bones, slender thighs, long eyelashes, and luscious, ruby lips. Prospective parents will have to pay a hefty sum if they want their children to comply with contemporary tastes in beauty. Even parents whose good breeding already assures a lovely child must pay a licensing fee for the use of any gene that has already been patented by Genie.

The benefits of this genetic bounty are not limited to procreation. New research has enabled the insertion of genetic material into existing cells. Genie claims this technological breakthrough will lead not only to healing genetic-based illnesses, but will enable us to sculpt the perfect body, as well.

Initial forays into genetic modeling have hit a bit of a snag, however, as unforeseen results keep popping up with distressing frequency. We've all heard of the tomato injected with pig genes to give it a firm, round shape, which grew a curly tail and a bristly snout! It now appears that genetic engineering has a ways to go before it provides precise (or consistent) rewards.

These unintended consequences reflect the grim humor of the genies we know from antiquity. You'd better be careful what you wish for! A woman who asked for blue eyes had her desire granted; however, the unexpected outcome of this request was that she now has blue eyes, to be sure—but rather than replacing her perfectly functional hazel eyes, the blue eyes were added to her forehead! The new look is rather dazzling, in a bug-eyed way.

Other genetic reconstructions gone awry have produced thin thighs holding up rather hefty hips; an extra, nicely trimmed nose alongside the old, still serviceable, but bulbous one; copious hair covering the entire body, instead of on top; and a handsome smile with pearly whites gracing a chiseled chin—just below the still-existing gap-toothed mouth with its tobacco-stained incisors.

Nevertheless, Genie has tried to reassure the public that these unfortunate occurrences in no way reflect the true promise of its vast array of genetic improvements. Why just last week, they discovered how to turn off the gene that turns hair prematurely gray! Unfortunately, it appears that the gene that makes our hair go gray is the very same gene that grants us a certain amount of wisdom as we age.

Of course, everyone knows that wisdom is wasted on the young—but who needs wisdom when you've got beauty? Think about the advantages! As you grow older, you can look eternally youthful, and still be just as foolish!

Statue Forbids Sex Education

GRANITE BAY, CALIFORNIA: A tempest roared ashore in this tiny coastal town when students from the high school newspaper interviewed their health ed teacher about the woeful state of students' reproductive knowledge. She told them a boy in her class had asked where his cervix was, and a girl wanted to know if she could get pregnant from oral sex.

Apparently this was too much for the Pacific Justice Institute, which charged the teacher with "sexual misconduct" for discussing sex with student reporters. They threatened to sue the teacher who "gave information to students about contraception and sexual activities in violation of a California *statue*."

I pondered this curious incident, wondering which statue had been violated? And did the statue realize that Pacific Justice was speaking on its behalf? I set out on a journey to clarify this inexplicable quandary.

California is a pretty large state, with a good number of statues. How to find the one that had allegedly been violated? It seemed like a Herculean task to touch base with every statue in the state. So I thought long and hard about how to winnow the field to a manageable level of inquiries.

The first one who came to mind was Father Junipero Serra, who might be especially concerned about contraception being taught in the schools. Of course there are a number of Serras at the Missions he founded, but probably the biggest statue is located off highway 280 just south of San Francisco, alongside the old Camino Real. Located at a rest stop notorious for its cruisy restroom and wooded area, I was sure this Father would have an opinion or two.

"Father," I said (even though I'm not Catholic, I decided it would be polite to address him as Father), "were you the statue who felt violated by this teacher's description of students' reproductive ignorance?"

He looked at me, a little surprised. Because so few passers by take it upon themselves to address him directly, most people don't realize he's capable of speech. He said, "I'm much too preoccupied with the antics at this reststop to be worried about sex education. If these closeted husbands had learned a little more about their own sexuality, they'd have somewhere else to go with their paramours and leave my bushes in peace. Did someone say I had a problem with it?"

"Not you, particularly, but apparently some statue felt violated."

"Well, it wasn't me."

I thanked him for his time, and continued on my quest. I checked in with the Virgin Mary (she's never heard a thing about sex education); Sutter at Sutter's Mill (though I figured that was a bit of a stretch, being a gold miner and all, he must have been pretty worldly, but you never know); I asked Shakespeare in Golden Gate Park, but of course another no; I tried a few pioneers at Donner Pass, but they were far too absorbed by their own trauma to have taken any notice of this trifle; I approached some Greek statues at the Getty in Malibu, but they thought it was a silly question; likewise, an Ohlone hunting in a diorama display at an east bay museum couldn't fathom how such natural functions could be offensive to anyone.

I went out to the coast and sat by the bluff overlooking the Golden Gate Bridge, my chin in hand, wondering who else could have taken such umbrage. Suddenly, I had an inspiration! I turned around and entered the courtyard of the Palace of the Legion of Honor, and there enshrined upon his solid rock sat Rodin's *The Thinker*.

Surely he might shed some insight on this perplexing puzzle! As I approached the thoughtful sculpture, I hesitated interrupting someone so deeply absorbed in contemplation. "O Thinker," I said, uncertain how to address such an imposing figure, "was it you who felt violated by the teacher's lament over her students' reproductive ignorance?"

He turned to me, looking annoyed. I immediately apologized for intruding on what was obviously some deep, philosophical rumination, but he brushed this aside. "Oh, those idiots, they got it all wrong, as usual. I didn't say I felt violated by the teacher's explanation, I said it was her right to free speech that was being violated by their silly threat to sue her for stating an obvious fact—namely, that her students were woefully ignorant of some basic reproductive knowledge. Why those nitwits got their shorts in a wad over something as innocent as that is totally beyond my ken. And they have the gall to claim that I was the statue being violated? It's utter nonsense. Now where was I?"

He dismissed me with a wave of his hand. I left, sorry to bother him, but at last I'd clarified this curious riddle: Pacific Justice had obviously misconstrued the true intent of this statue.

The Thinker immediately returned to his previous posture, chin in hand, no doubt pondering profound thoughts about life's ultimate meaning.

webcamgirl.com

OHH! MORNING AGAIN—hello, world! Uhmm, it's nice to stretch, I feel so lazy, I could stay in bed all day long! But, lots to do today, gotta get up and on my way!

Do you like my new negligee? I hope so, because your subscriptions paid for it! That's what I like about working my way through college—having nice things, living in a sumptuous apartment like this instead of that ratty old dorm. Who could study there, with all the goings on in that place! If it wasn't boys running up and down the hall yelling like maniacs, it was techno music blasting all night long, police sirens, and riots after football games! Who needs it?

Each day when I get up, before I make my bed up, I pray my little prayer to you! And you, and you, and *you*! It's true, every single day, because I am so grateful to each and every one of you! Boop boop be doo! I no longer feel lonely, because I know every minute of the day or night, someone is looking at me. It's so comforting to know the whole world is watching!

I never understood this hangup about privacy. Privacy means being alone, and I never want to be alone! I love having someone to talk to, to come home to, to snuggle up with at the end of a long, hard day. I keep my webcam right by my face when I go to sleep, its little eye ever so vigilant over me, it's like Jesus in a way!

Even with intimate functions, I don't have anything to hide! It's just natural. I love taking a shower, whoosh! Feel the spray, the silky soap, the luxurious shampoo lather! I feel like I'm in a Dove commercial!

I get very excited when a boy comes over to visit me. I never say anything about the webcam. I figure he already knows about it, and that's why he's here—or else he doesn't have a clue and if I told him he'd just get all freaked out and self-conscious and wouldn't be able to do a thing!

Being watched adds this special thrill to sex, because I'm both in it and vicariously watching it at the same time, anticipating the very same thrills you are! Plus, later I can watch it over and over again. Knowing whatever boy I'm with is either into it too, or totally oblivious, just adds to the fun. I like to carry on—pretend I'm a tiger—rowr, rowr! Scratch his back, or make him mount me doggy style. I scream and wriggle and toss and crow! *Woo hoo*!

I love my new vanity! All the round little bulbs surrounding my mirror are so flattering—never a shadow shall cross my face! Hmm, what shall I wear today? It's so warm out, let's see—this tangerine halter top is lots of fun, with a short aqua skirt, and my new Gucci sandals. Perfect! Mirror mirror on the wall, I luvvums you! Mwa!

I know sometimes my life must seem pretty boring. Like here I am eating a bowl of cereal—how mundane! Yet sustenance is part of life, and anyway I never liked eating alone! Now I don't have to anymore. We can talk about current events, the Big Game, la de la, frankly I never cared much for sports but I'm totally stoked by the enthusiasm of the spectators, only sometimes they get so rowdy, it's awesome. I'd rather just watch them on TV, overturning cars and setting them on fire, that's my favorite.

Even after I finish college, get married, and settle down with kids of my own, I'll never give this up. Webcam started out as a clever scam just to get through school, but now it's taking over my life! My Postmodern Cultural Studies prof has seen my show—in fact he watches me all the time! He says I've created a whole new art form: a self-reflexive, real-time blogger journal, crossing the boundary between the watcher and the watched—it's like my very own *Real World*!

Here's my notebook—I'm working on my senior thesis. It's called *All About Me*—wouldn't you know! I explain how I exist within a particular historical, social, and cultural nexus. My website is really a deconstruction of what's uniquely me!

I'm seriously considering my webcam life as my new career. I started out majoring in architecture, but now I think of myself as the architect of my own soul! I love your emails saying how

I've touched your hearts, it's so encouraging! And what could be more gratifying than reaching across the virtual void and really touching someone?

Oops, I'm running late! But don't worry, now that I've got my webcam palmpilot, you can follow me anywhere! No more of this dead air time while I'm off to school, shopping, or getting my hair done! You can still be with me while I pursue my higher education: listen to my scintillating insights about political correctness, help me struggle through postfeminist rhetoric, or rig up a new marketing plan for my webpage!

Tonight I've got another date with Tim, that hunkabunk. I'm going over to his place, and this time, you get to come along, too! See you there! See you everywhere!

Man Bites Head Off Son's Coach

SPRINGFIELD, ILLINOIS: This town is reeling from the shock of a recent incident of "sports rage," when a man went so far as to bite the head off his son's coach for benching him during the league basketball finals.

Billy, the star forward, was called on a foul for the third time in the final quarter, when his coach decided to bench him. "You're a gunner, Billy, but you need to chill out." Just points behind a record for the season, with agents from colleges all over the country watching the big game, Billy's father blew a gasket.

Shoving spectators out of his way as he stormed through the bleachers, he reached the court and laid into the coach. "What the hell do you think you're doing? Put my son back in the game!"

The coach tried to reason with him. "He's committed three fouls in the last ten minutes! He needs to get ahold of himself—and so do you, sir."

Well, that did it. That's when Billy's dad flew into what can only be called an explosive rage. He grabbed the coach by the shoulders and opened his jaws wider than seemed humanly possible, then, with a thundering roar, he bit off the coach's head!

Pandemonium broke loose as the coach's head rolled across the court, and his body flopped about on the floor spurting blood from his neck like a geyser. Dozens of spectators were trampled as the crowd stampeded away from the spray in utter horror.

Referees blew their whistles trying to restore order, while Billy's dad, covered with blood, wandered about in a daze. It was obvious that the full impact of what he had just done had not yet sunk in.

During the stunned silence that followed, Billy grabbed the coach's head, dribbled it down the court and executed a handy lay-up, to the astonishment of his team-mates, who stood around gaping at each other. Understandably, no one offered the boy a high-five, or patted his butt for making the basket. It was, after all, a relatively clear shot.

The police arrived immediately to arrest Billy's dad, who offered little resistance. Five ambulances were needed to take those who were injured by the stampede. Afterward, local news teams arrived and tried to make sense of the explosive carnage that had taken place during this all-American game.

Jack Spencer, the team captain, said "When the coach benched Billy, I thought his dad might have given him a good chewing out, but no one really expected him to actually bite his head off."

"I don't care how good a gunner he is," another one of Billy's teammates said. "If he's fouling every which way, elbowing other guys in the ribs, knocking them on their cans, Billy deserved to be benched."

A boy on the visiting team said "It seems way over the top, to me. I think biting the coach's head off is pretty excessive."

A mother whose daughter was injured by the stampede said "It's only a game. I thought the whole point of playing a sport was to have fun!"

"There's just too much at stake nowadays," one of the referees told the interviewer. "Everything's riding on the one-in-a-thousand chance some kid's going to get picked for a college team."

"People lose perspective," added the coach from the visiting team. "Is it winning at all costs? What kind of example is this going to be for good sportsmanship? We want to win, sure; but the main point is to do your best, play by the rules, and have a good time. But then you got these crazed parents breathing down your neck, chewing you out, or biting your head off—literally, as in this tragic case. It's enough to make you want to find another job."

Not surprisingly, Billy failed to get a single offer from any of the college reps.

Virgins Take the Pledge

BILLINGS, MONTANA: In a public celebration of Abstinence Week, over one hundred girls at St. Theresa's took a vow of celibacy until marriage. All dressed in white, they took turns coming up to the podium to affirm their chastity. Sister George presided over the ceremony, and surveyed the assembled virgins with a look of contented beatitude.

Afterward, we talked with some of the young women about their intentions. Nancy, a slender blonde and head cheerleader, said "I don't want to feel pressured to have sex before I'm ready. By taking the pledge, I'm endorsing a strict, no-nonsense, hands-off policy."

Linda, with horn-rimmed glasses and dark hair that covered most of her face, presented herself as a serious academic achiever. She nodded in agreement. "I want to be able to look into my future husband's eyes and tell him that I saved myself only for him."

Mary, swinging her arms to the rhythms of the music from her headphones, said "We hereby serve notice to all boys to keep their cotton-pickin', finger-lickin', chicken-pluckin' mittens to themselves. That's what I say!"

Another clutch of girls, who were no longer technically virgins, still affirmed their intention to save themselves from any further degradation by boys who only want one thing. Justine said, "Everyone knows a boy will drop you as soon as he gets what he wants. We've learned from our mistakes, and we stand in solidarity with our sisters!"

Gina, one of the girls who had not yet joined the circle of abstinence, gazed off into the distance, a sly grin curling the corner of her mouth. "All the more for me," she whispered, to no one in particular.

A year later, we returned to Saint Theresa's to see how our virgins were faring with their chastity pledge. We were able to assemble most of the same girls we originally interviewed for a follow-up discussion.

So, how's it going? Were you able to keep your pledge not to have sex before marriage?

Nancy, who had blossomed into a full-figured young woman, turned slightly away. "Well, it kind of depends on what you mean by 'sex.'"

After Monica Lewinsky, I expected a certain amount of quibbling about the true definition of "having sex," but I was frankly unprepared for the Talmudic disputation exhibited by this group of ostensible virgins.

Why don't you tell me what you mean by "sex"? You're the ones who took the pledge, after all.

Mary, arms still swinging to another tune on her Walkman, said "I think making out's okay. As long as it doesn't lead to anything else."

Linda, looking a little shy, her hair covering her face even more than it had last year, said "Well, um, what do you think about heavy petting?"

Justine, the stalwart defender of the virtue of former virgins, said " 'Heavy petting,' that is so retro! No one's used that term since the sixties!"

Linda looked at Justine through a space in her hair. "Well, don't you think if you really like a boy, it's okay if he touches your breasts?"

"Yes," Justine said. "So long as he doesn't make you touch *him*, you know where."

"Well I don't know," Nancy said. "I mean as long as there's no danger of actual penetration, which is what we're really talking about here, then I don't see why it's such a problem if you touch him back."

"Well where did you touch him?" Mary asked, obviously intrigued.

Nancy blushed. "Well, you know. Down there."

The other girls gasped.

"Well why's that so bad?"

Justine said, "Don't you know what that could lead to? Once you start touching that part of a boy, he'll get aroused and then accuse you of being a prick-tease if you don't put out."

"Well that's not necessarily the case," Nancy said.

Linda said, "I think I know what Nancy's talking about."

"Well what *is* Nancy talking about? That's what I'd like to know," Mary said, her hands on her hips. She had stopped swaying to the music by now, and in fact had taken off her headphones, not wanting to miss a thing.

Nancy reddened. "What if you touch a boy, you know, with your lips. That's not really sex, is it?"

"No!" Linda shook her head vehemently, her face nearly disappearing in a cascade of hair. We had never seen her express her opinions so strongly before. "No," she repeated from inside her tent, "it's definitely not sex."

"Well of course kissing isn't sex," Mary said.

Nancy fiddled with her pom pom. "But what if you touch him with your lips—down there. That's not really sex."

Justine drew a quick intake of breath. " 'Touch him with your lips!' Are you saying a blow job isn't sex?" she demanded. "You sound just like Bill Clinton!"

"Well it's not!" Linda chimed in. "There's certainly no danger of getting pregnant, if that's what you're so worried about." Linda's face emerged from her curtain of hair. "The boy's happy as a clam, and he doesn't just leave you once he's gotten what he wanted; in fact, he keeps coming back for more! And you've still got your reputation! Isn't that the best of both worlds?"

"What kind of reputation is *that*!" Mary looked totally shocked. "I cannot believe what I'm hearing. All this past year, I've been pure as the driven snow, and you two have been sucking off the entire football team from St. Ignatius?"

"Not the whole team," Nancy said, quietly.

"Anyways," Linda said, "I think even if there's a little penetration, it shouldn't really count as sex if the boy doesn't come. Especially if he's wearing a condom."

"Linda!" Mary said. "Wearing a condom is a sin! That's interfering with the Lord's special plan!"

"Why should it be such a sin if it keeps you from getting pregnant? Isn't getting pregnant before marriage a sin?"

"Of course it is!" Mary said. "That's the whole reason we took the pledge! And now you're trying to wriggle your way out of it with your stupid definitions!"

"I'm not!" Linda said.

"That's right, we're not," Nancy added. "The whole point of abstinence is not to get pregnant, so what difference does it make if we come up with some pretty creative ways around it?"

"The whole point of abstinence was to save ourselves for marriage!" Mary exclaimed. "You said so yourself, Linda. You stood right here a year ago and said you wanted to gaze into your future husband's eyes and tell him you saved yourself for only him!"

"Well I have, for the most part," Linda said. "The only part that matters, anyway. I'm not going to let anyone else get me pregnant, that's for sure."

Justine jumped back in. "Well girls. I am totally astounded. What you and Nancy are essentially saying is that oral sex and sex with condoms are both okay because you won't get pregnant, and besides it's not really sex anyway, is that it?"

Linda looked at Nancy, and Nancy looked at Linda, and they both shrugged. Nancy said, "Well yes, I don't think those things you mentioned are really sex, that's all."

"No, not at all," Linda said, lifting her head so that her hair fell away from her face for the first time. "Sexual intercourse is when you go all the way, with orgasms and everything, in order to get pregnant."

Justine said "So it's not sex if you're using a diaphragm, or you're on the pill? That would mean practically no one in all of Billings Montana is having sex, except when they're trying to get pregnant!"

Linda backed down. "No, I guess that would still be sex. But I don't see why sex with a condom should count. That way you won't even get STDs. Or AIDS."

"So all those gay guys having safe sex are not really having sex?" Justine said.

"Well how could two boys really have sexual intercourse, anyway?" Mary asked. "Isn't that a contradiction in terms?"

"That's right!" Nancy said. "Sex is between a man and a woman, for the purpose of having a baby. Otherwise it isn't really even sex!"

Linda said, "Maybe the whole trouble with this discussion is that we all started out with a different definition of sex."

"No, Linda," Justine said, "the whole trouble with this discussion is that you're no longer a virgin, and you won't even admit it!"

"I never went all the way," Linda said. "I was just supposing, for the sake of argument."

"But you had oral sex!" insisted Justine.

"Like we said, that's not really sex. Huh, Nancy?"

Nancy shook her head. "No, oral sex is definitely not sexual intercourse."

"What would Sister George say?" Mary asked.

Of course everyone knew the answer to this question, but no one had invited Sister George to our little meeting. They all sat in silence, avoiding Mary's eyes.

I was curious, however, to find out what Gina thought, whom most of the girls had shunned last year for not taking the pledge, and who had been silent during this entire discussion.

So what do you think, Gina?

Gina wore a slinky black dress, her short auburn hair crowning her head in an attractive, Caesar-like cut. She lifted her chin, cocking her head to one side, a sultry smile appearing on her dark, red lips. "Welcome to the club," she said.

B.R.A. Denounces Brutal Bug-Eating Ritual

PORTLAND, OREGON: Bugs' Rights Advocates have condemned the annual bug-eating contest that takes place each year on a warm spring day at Reed, the notoriously avant garde college nestled away in this otherwise quiet town in the Pacific northwest.

Carrying signs such as *Protect Our Creepy Crawlers*, *Invertebrates Have Feelings, Too*, and *Be Kind to Bugs*, they marched along the perimeter of the rally as the bug-eaters made their preparations to go on stage. Drums set up an incessant beat that caused the party-goers and prospective bug-eaters to dance in an ever-increasing frenzy.

A spokesman with a megaphone tried to stop the impending slaughter by appealing to the conscience of this otherwise liberal student body. "It's one thing to hunt out of necessity, but quite another to kill innocent creatures out of sheer sport," he intoned.

"We're not shooting Bambi, we're eating bugs!" one fellow called out, clad only in wet underwear. "Have a beer!" another shouted, holding two bottles over his head. A third student squirted the spokesman with a water gun. "Get soaked!"

"Grub-eating for fun is atavistic, primitive chic!" the spokesman continued, dodging the spray.

"Says who? John the Baptist ate locusts and honey!" this bearded, shirtless youth shouted back, and everyone roared their approval.

The bug advocates linked arms and chanted: "Stop Torturing Bugs! Stop Torturing Bugs! Stop Torturing Bugs!"

The crowd shouted back: "Eat Bugs Now! Eat Bugs Now! Eat Bugs Now!"

The female MC, her hennaed hair flaming red, held aloft a bowl and shouted, "Who wants to eat some grubs and tobacco worm pupae?"

John the Baptist leapt onto the stage and grabbed some grubs and gulped them down. He shoved another fistful into his mouth, growling as he crunched the pupae, while green goo dribbled down his beard. Then he clutched the MC to his chest and tried to kiss her. "EEEWWW!" squealed all the women.

A couple of bouncers pulled the grub-eater off the stage. The MC wiped her mouth, then licked her fingers. "Yum!" she said. "That's grody!" They all cheered her for being such a good sport.

"Next up, who's gonna eat worms?" She held aloft a bowl that overflowed with squirming pink and gray vermicelli.

A bunch of rowdies chanted in unison: "Brad-ley! Brad-ley! Brad-ley! Brad-ley!" and pushed this guy toward the front of the stage. Finally, Brad hoisted himself onto the platform. He pushed out his lower lip, looking dejected, then started to sing: "Nobody likes me, everybody hates me, guess I'll eat some wor-er-erms."

Apparently, this had been a long-time tradition, because everyone immediately joined in: "Long thin slimy ones, short fat juicy ones, itsy-bitsy fuzzy wuzzy worms!"

He took a swig of beer to steel himself for the ordeal. He leaned backward to the sound of a drum roll, while one by one, the MC lowered worms into his gaping craw.

The whole tribe joined the chant: "Down goes the first worm, down goes the second worm, Oh! how they wiggle and they squir-er-erm! Long thin slimy ones, short fat juicy ones, itsy-bitsy fuzzy wuzzy worms!"

The worm-eater raised his head and peered across the sea of faces, looking mournful and a little sick. "Nobody likes me, everybody hates me, Oh! how I wish I hadn't eaten those worms!" He rubbed his tummy and shook his head in mock despair, while everyone sang the chorus: "Long thin slimy ones, short fat juicy ones, itsy-bitsy fuzzy wuzzy worms!"

Brad pretended to vomit: "Uhhh-up comes the first worm, uhh-up comes the second worm, Oh! how they wiggle and the squir-er-erm!"

Then the final chorus: "Long thin slimy ones, short fat juicy ones, itsy-bitsy fuzzy wuzzy worms!"

But instead of spitting up, which would have been gross enough, we watched as a single worm parted his lips, waved about blindly in the air, and slid down his chin. Squeals and screams accompanied this display as one worm after another slithered out of Brad's mouth, until he had a dozen worms hanging and wriggling from his lips.

"*Eeewww*!"

The bug advocate shouted through his megaphone: "We condemn this sadistic mastication of innocent worms!"

"Yeah, you and your grandma!" hooted back the carousing party animals, many of whom were drenched with the beers they happily tossed back and forth, spraying one another with eruptions of carbonated brew.

The spokesman turned to the other pro-bug sign-holder. "They're simply goading each other by leaps and bounds to gross-out their fellow students."

"It's mob mentality, the worst kind of peer pressure, like hazing," she agreed, shaking her head sadly. "And at the expense of innocent creatures."

Just then, a bare-chested rooster strutted onstage, wearing gym shorts with feathers gracing his arms, a vermilion comb tied to his head, a yellow beak attached to his forehead, a tail of feathers, and boots with spurs. "I am a splendid cock, I crow every morn at dawn! And then at dusk I poke my head through my girlfriend's doorway!" He sidled up to the MC, resting his head on her shoulder. The audience cheered.

Then, his head bobbing, he pecked at the plate of crickets on the table, scooping them up with his tongue and eagerly chewing them. But this was pretty tame, compared to what was next in store for this cocky bug-eater.

The MC held aloft a tiny wire cage. "And now it's time for the *piece de resistance*!"

The crowd started chanting "Hoo ha! Hoo ha! Hoo ha! Hoo ha!"

"The Madagascar Hissing Cockroach!"

The audience hissed with menacing pleasure: "Sssssss! Sssssssss!"

Next came a drum roll, and two other youths jumped on stage. They crouched on either side of the rooster, counting "One, two, three!" and yanked down his shorts to the sound of a clanging cymbal. The rooster stood naked, elbows akimbo, his cock dangling freely in the warm spring breeze.

Then they took two huge, menacing cockroaches out of the wire cage, their antennae searching the air, and placed them alongside the guy's dick, which by now had engorged itself in a partial erection, no doubt responding to the excitement of the rally (to say nothing of the tickling sensation from the roaches' prickly legs).

The rooster gyrated his hips, the hissing cockroaches clinging to his boner as it wagged back and forth. "EAT MY COCK ROACH!" he bellowed.

The students picked up the chant: "Eat my cock roach! Eat my cock roach! Eat my cock roach!" until the two guys knelt down and munched on the roaches, their lips briefly grazing the shaft of the rooster's penis.

The throng went wild! The roach-eaters turned toward the crowd, the cockroaches crunched between their teeth, legs and antennae waving in tortured anguish. Drums pounded while the rooster showed off his woody and crowed "Cock-a-doodle-doo!" The revelers danced and whooped, whistling and hollering, stomping in a storm of orgiastic and homoerotic rapture.

Meanwhile, the Bugs' Rights Advocates had slunk away, dispirited and downcast in their quest to dampen the enthusiasm of this crazed, bug-eating hysteria.

Football Fever Sweeps Nation as Spontaneous Prayers Defy the Supreme Court

WOOSTER, OHIO: In a rally before a recent football game at Bigelow High School, the Reverend Chuck Comstock denounced the Supreme Court ruling in *Santa Fe School District v. Doe* that student-led prayers before football games were unconstitutional. "The Court says when we pray at football games we're 'imposing our will' on others. But the Chief Justice said the majority opinion 'bristles with hostility to all things religious in public life.' It's high time Bible-believing Christians stood up to be counted! Statistics will show you that the team that has the most prayers usually wins. Besides, without God, how can you expect to score in the Big Game of Life?"

Buddy Stillwater, the Crusaders' wide receiver, agreed. "When the Lord's Prayer comes over the loudspeaker, you can actually feel the positive energy flowing from the crowd. Of course, you still gotta practice, but you're a lot more likely to complete a pass with a prayer in your heart. Now, though, ever since student-led prayer was forbidden? It's like, subversive. In the midst of a huddle, the quarterback will pray, 'Let's score this one for Jesus!' The other guys slap his ass and say, 'Fuckin' A! We're gonna cream their butts!' It's like our own secret prayer circle."

"Thataboy, Buddy!" Chuck said, and clapped him on the back. Buddy hustled down to the field, and the Reverend took the microphone to address the stadium. "We started out as one nation under God," he intoned. "Then we got diversity, pitting every kind of atheistic kook against wholesome, red-blooded Americans. I say, it's a crying shame to forbid our right to pray at football games. Don't let the Supreme Court take away our religious freedom!

"Miss Tiffany Barnes is going to sing us the National Anthem, while everyone stands with their right hand over their hearts, just like we always do. Then, in the very next moment, who knows? Maybe, without any orchestration or coercion on the part of the school authorities, some of the spectators might spontaneously feel moved to pray and give praise to the Lord! Right out loud! And who do you think's gonna try and stop us?"

"Nobody!" the crowd shouted back, and after the anthem, a solemn rendition of the Lord's Prayer echoed through the stadium.

After the prayer, whistles blew, the band played, and both teams took their positions on the field. The Reverend turned back to this reporter. "Did the stadium collapse just 'cause we said a prayer?" he asked. "You know, believers are a tolerant bunch. Why, we won't be offended if someone doesn't feel like praying along with us. Hottentots and Hindus, Hebrews and Voodoos, they're all welcome to say their own prayers. Christians recognize the fact that not everyone's gonna root for the home team. The tent of the Lord is big enough for everyone!"

During the game, Buddy scored his team's only touchdown, intercepting a miraculous "Hail Mary" in the endzone. He spiked the ball in triumph, then knelt and bowed his head, placing his hands together in a defiant gesture of prayer. The cheerleaders cried out a spontaneous cheer: "Jesus loves you we can tell—'cause He thinks you're mighty swell!" Buddy stood up, and lifted his index finger toward heaven. The crowd went wild, yelling and stomping their approval while Buddy's extra point kick sailed over the goal post, tying the score.

Then later, when the Braves kept up their advances in one skirmish after another, the girls shouted "Come on, Crusaders! Push 'em back, push 'em back, waaaay back!"

In the end, however, the Crusaders lost to the Braves, 7 to 14.

Man Kills Gay Dog

ROANOKE, VIRGINIA: Joe Schiffer, 53, was arrested today for cruelty to animals in the death of Freddy, his wife's French poodle. He flung the poor dog against a tree, breaking his neck, after Freddy was humped by a German Shepherd.

"The goddam dog's a fucking fag," he told the cops, as if this justified his conduct. Apparently he'd taken the prize poodle, his wife's show-dog, for a walk through the park. "This police dog sniffed his butt and climbed on top of him. Freddy just stood there and took it. He didn't growl, he didn't try to shake him off; he actually licked his chops like he was enjoying it!" Schiffer said, disgusted. "I had to beat the other dog off with a stick. Then Freddy went bounding after him, like he couldn't get enough of it! That's when I lost it."

His wife was heartbroken, and in fact was the one who pressed charges against her husband. When I caught up with him at the city jail, he was still fuming.

"It's her own goddam fault. She's the one who gave him that ridiculous coquette coif—the ruffle around his shoulders, the poofy top-knot, those fruit-cake cuffs around the ankles, the pom-pom at the end of his tail, and worse yet, they shaved his butt! Like some fag-bait fanny-boy, waving his naked ass in the air, no wonder all the other dogs wanted to jump his bones! Christ, I almost wanted to fuck him myself! Then she struts him around these shows like some pompadour prostitute, for crying out loud, what did she expect?"

Mr. Schiffer, it appears you have little remorse for what you've done. Do you really think the dog deserved to be hurled against a tree, and killed?

"Any self-respecting dog is better off dead than going through life with what that dog had to put up with. Strutting through his paces with his prissy poodle-trainer every single morning, off to the groomer three times a week to shave his ass! The dog never got to romp and play 'cause *he might get dirty*," he sneered. "I don't know what she expected me to do when every dog in the goddam park's trying to bang his butt, and he's sitting there taking it, admiring his faggy nail polish!"

Do you think your dog's really gay?

"How could he not be a homo? He's a goddam poodle! You ever seen a poodle that'll stand up and defend his territory? There's no bark in him, much less bite. He loved prancing around the ring like some Queen of Sheba, showing off his bobbed tail! Freddy was as Nellie as they come, and when I seen him getting buggered with that queer grin on his face, I couldn't take it no more."

You know, Mr. Schiffer, you're in serious trouble. You could get a pretty hefty fine, plus a couple of years in jail. And your wife wants a divorce.

"Well if that's the price I gotta pay to rid the world of one fag dog, then so be it. I've done my part. Give me a Doberman pinscher any day of the week. Now there's a real dog! He'll lunge for your goddam throat if you look at him sidewise. And my wife? That strumpet. She can just screw herself with one of her pansy poodle-trainers, as far as I'm concerned."

Gullibility Has a Legitimate Role in Civic Life, Politician Claims

WACO, TEXAS: On a stump speech testing the waters for a Presidential bid, George W. Flatbush announced his new plan to enlist programs based on unverifiable beliefs to get people off welfare.

"Belief without evidence is a virtue," he said. "Why, you can convince almost anyone of something once you show them proof. What kind of achievement is that? The real challenge is to convince someone of something when there's no justification at all!"

Flatbush supporters cheered, while others stood around scratching their heads, looking a little puzzled.

"What takes a real leap of faith is to believe in something, anything, really, it hardly matters what, so long as there's no real evidence to prove it! Remember, absence of evidence is not evidence of absence. As a matter of fact, the more outlandish the claim, the greater the test of your faith. And believe you me, your faith will be sorely tested by my campaign—so don't misunderestimate me!"

His speech was interrupted by a spontaneous eruption of applause, followed by a spirited rendition of *The Saints Come Marching In* by a local Salvation Army band. They had a big bass drum, a tuba, and a trombone, which was slightly out of tune.

"The less reasons you can come up with to support your view, the more demanding the claims of faith. The harder it is to believe, the more precious the believer!"

The candidate unveiled a new program of public funding for church-sponsored charities. "It's been shown time and again that programs based on supernatural beliefs provide relief from welfare, whereas the government just creates more bureaucracy, more dependency. Meet Mandy Glenn, a man who was injured at work, but then he voluntarily took himself off disability!"

Mandy was rolled onto the stage in his wheelchair, while the crowd hollered their approval. "Give me a prayer rather than a welfare check, any day of the week," he declared. "A prayer lifts me up, whereas a welfare check just drags me down and fills me with self-contempt."

Flatbush clapped him on the back. "Thank you Mandy, for that elegant testimonial. You see, what we have here is a new plan for getting government regulators off our backs. If you need to breathe clean air, get yourself an air filter! If you want good drinking water, drink bottled water! If you want a park, go buy a forest. If a road needs fixing, find your own road! Or sell the road to a private company, they'll for darn sure take care of it. If you get sick, just ask your family to pray for you. If you need gas for your car, drill yourself an oil well! That's exactly what my daddy did.

"Rarely is the question asked: *Is our children learning?* But the answer is simple: If you want an education, read a book! If you need a paycheck, get a job. I know how hard it is for you to put food on your family, but the free market will take care of almost everyone. To make sure no one's left out in the cold, we oughtta cut taxes to make the pie higher, so you can scoop off the frosting!"

Flatbush surveyed his audience with a big smile. "Remember, superstition is the basis of all morality! I think if you say you're going to do something and don't do it, that's trustworthiness. We need more supernaturally-based initiatives for our communities."

Mr. Flatbush, would you say that you're an advocate of anti-disestablishmentarianism?

"Watch your language young man, this is a family-rated campaign stop!" Flatbush admonished me. Then his aide leaned forward to whisper in his ear.

"What's that? Against the separation of church and state?" He turned back to the audience. "Well if that's what you're against, then I'm all for it," he said. "Just don't ask me how to spell it!" The band played, and Flatbush said, "Remember, the American people wants a president that appeals to the angels!" Then he waved, and gave us his famous smirk.

After the speech, I took a survey of folks to gauge their reaction to Flatbush's run for President. Most were pretty impressed with his rhetoric, although they thought he was a little short on the details.

"I like the notion of not paying so many taxes," a farmer named Frank Gibbons told me. "But I don't care so much for the idea of digging my own sewer system. Or my own grave, for that matter."

Mrs. Willow said, "He seems very polite. I wouldn't mind having him over for Sunday dinner."

I asked a man named Austin, an accountant from town, what he thought about Flatbush's plan to get people off welfare.

"A song and a prayer'll only get you so far," he commented. "I'm not so sure where he thinks all this good will is going to come from. If a man can work, that's one thing. But what about seniors, kids, or the disabled? There's some things that cost money, like health care, and money doesn't grow on trees. Will Flatbush let Mandy move in with him till he gets back on his feet? That would be a real test of private charity, right there."

Another man, who had been listening to our conversation, said "Well, I agree with most of what Flatbush said. You gotta believe in something, 'cause otherwise there's all these things we can't explain! Isn't it better to believe, than to live your whole life in confusion?"

Why Men Don't Call

ATLANTA: Researchers have reported that male rats deficient in a hormone called *oxytocin* sniff a previous mating partner as if they'd never met her before, giving rise to the suspicion that the hormone plays a key role in mate selection, womanizing, and what's commonly described as creepoid behavior in human males.

You know the scenario: you meet him in a fern bar, he seems nice enough: he doesn't just talk about himself, he asks about you; and he smells okay. So all right, he doesn't sweep you off your feet, but maybe he'll grow on you. You're surprised how good he is in bed. The next morning he says "I'll call you," and you actually believe it this time—there was something special between you—he even said so himself. But of course he never calls.

You run into him again at a party. When introduced, he acts as though he's never met you. You give him the cold shoulder. "What?" he asks.

"Get away from me, you two-timing creepoid."

"Have we met before?"

You roll your eyes, even more disgusted by his duplicity—but wait! The guy says, "Oh my God, it's happened again!"

This time, you say "What?"

"I'm oxytocin deficient, and I have a hard time recognizing women I've already slept with. I am so embarrassed. I know it's asking a lot, but could you ever find it in your heart to forgive me?"

You're surprised by his odd apology, and for a brief moment consider whether you'd give him a second chance. Then he says, "You seem like a nice enough girl; in fact, I have the sneaking suspicion there could be something very special between us."

At this point you mumble something unintelligible and make your escape—he obviously has serious problems, and you're just as glad he never called you.

Gay men are just as bad about calling. Maybe worse. At least a straight man will come on to the same woman twice. Whereas, when you run into a gay guy you've already had sex with, he'll act as if he doesn't know you—but instead of coming on to you again, he'll ignore you! As if any contacts you had in the past—that romantic hump in the bushes; that tender blowjob in the video booth—were regrettable mistakes.

Now, why would a gay man spurn any guy he's already had sex with? You'd think he'd want to take advantage of their availability. Constantly seeking out new partners spreads around his sperm, but what kind of evolutionary advantage is that?

Men are like rats, in a way—maybe in more ways than one.

Ex-Gay Caught Red-Faced in Gay Bar

WASHINGTON, D.C.: John Poke, "ex-gay" poster boy for the "gays can go straight" crowd, was discovered recently chatting up some guys at Mr. P's, a well-known gay bar in Dupont Circle.

Bobby, a former ex-gay who recognized him from the cover of *Newsweek*, said "John, you look familiar. Maybe we've met before. What's your last name?"

"Puddentane," he lied.

"That's an unusual name. Are you sure your last name isn't *Poke*, you poker-faced liar?" Poke got up and started moving away from the table. "Admit it!" Bobby demanded.

"Ask me again and I'll tell you the same," Poke said, edging through the crowd toward the door.

When Bobby pulled out a camera and tried to take his picture, Poke squealed like a piglet and ducked behind another man. At this point, the bartender leapt into the fray to block the photo. He assumed Bobby was a potential blackmailer, harassing a closeted customer.

"Hey," said Bobby, "don't you know who that guy is?"

"It doesn't matter," said the bartender. "Our guests have a right to their privacy. Leave him alone!"

"That's John Poke, the ex-gay!"

Meanwhile, Poke squeezed past the bouncer, and Bobby clambered over the bar stools, rapidly clicking pictures, the flashes lighting up the bar like a strobe lamp. Poke ran outside, with Bobby speeding after him in hot pursuit. Bobby finally caught a photo of him, fleeing down the street, waving his hands frantically in the air. "Ex-gay my foot!" Bobby taunted. "You hokey-pokey hypocrite! When was the last time you got poked!"

EXIT, one of the nation's largest ex-gay groups, touted Poke as their poster boy, featured on the covers of *Newsweek* and

Time, during their infamous media campaign a couple of summers ago. Poke was their chief ex-gay spokesman, holding out hope for other gays that if they gave their hearts to Jesus, they really could go straight, just like he had; he'd even married a former lesbian.

"I was hopelessly, compulsively homosexual," Poke confessed at the time. "But with the help of Jesus, I turned away from that sordid lifestyle of degradation and sin, and never looked back. There's hope for you, too."

Melvin Mavis, EXIT's director, acknowledged that they're looking into the incident. "Knowing John as I do, just because he stepped into a gay bar doesn't necessarily mean he was looking for dick," Mavis said. "John used to flee his troubles by going out in drag as Divinity, the drag queen that every man loved and adored. It was kind of pathetic, the way he was used by men and then discarded, but he got lots of attention.

"If he just had a drink and socialized a little, that's one thing; but if he had genital contact with another man, that would absolutely bar him from his leadership role at EXIT. We'd strip him of his position as ex-gay spokesman, and he'd have to go back to rehab. After such a fall, he would need to start his straight conversion therapy all over again."

A few days later, when reached by telephone for comment, Poke claimed he merely stepped inside the bar to use the restroom, not even realizing it was a gay club. "When I figured out it was, I thought why not do a little research? So I sat down and had a drink. Yes, I chatted up a couple of guys, not to come on to them, but because I wanted to win their confidence. I was just about to bring up the fact that I was no longer gay myself, when this ruffian started shamelessly harassing me. Now I know what it's like to be gay-bashed! Imagine! And I'm not even gay!"

So you thought this was a good opportunity to convert some unhappy gays?

"I wouldn't go quite that far," Poke said. "But just because I happened into a gay bar certainly doesn't mean that I'm going back to the lifestyle. I must admit, being in a gay club felt a little nostalgic, but I really don't have any of those desires anymore."

What were you doing in the restroom?

"Excuse me? I'm not into T-room sex, if that's what you're insinuating."

You were busted, John; your cover was blown. Why don't you just come out? It could help a lot of other gays who are still struggling, just like you are.

"No, that's impossible. I told you, as I keep telling everyone, if anyone would ever listen, I'm no longer gay. I left that squalid, tormented life, and I have no intention of ever going back."

Are you claiming that all your desire for men has disappeared?

"Ever since Jesus came into my heart, I've been leading a life that's according to His plan as I've understood it. As you know, I'm married now to a wonderful girl and we're very much in love."

John, you didn't really answer my question. Can you honestly say you're no longer sexually aroused by the sight of a naked man?

There was a long pause. Then John cleared his throat and said, "Ask me no more questions and I'll tell you no more lies."

Botticelli Nabbed in Child Porno Bust

CINCINNATI: *Madonna in Glory*, a painting by Botticelli, was seized along with a dozen other works in a child porno trafficking sting this weekend. The curator of the Fine Arts Museum was arrested, along with several artists and photographers featured in the current exhibition: *Naked Virtue*, a show designed to portray childlike innocence.

At today's press conference, the police chief said "We're charging these scum bags with showing children in a state of licentious nudity, designed to appeal to the prurient interest of pedophiles."

But aren't these works of art? Botticelli, especially, is renowned for his portraits of the Madonna and Child. Similar paintings have been shown for centuries in the Uffizi Palace, and all the great cathedrals of Europe.

"Art, shmart!" the chief snapped. "It's child pornography! Look at this!" He held up the portrait of Mary holding the little baby Jesus. "Notice how the swaddling clothes are intentionally draped to expose the Christ Child's private parts. That's not only sacrilegious, it's a felony offense!"

I peered at the painting. The infant was draped with a sheer, gossamer-like material, so I couldn't quite make out his penis.

Isn't that just a fold in the fabric?

"No it's not!" He pointed at a tiny nub in the Christ Child's crotch. "If you look really close, it's totally graphic. That's the Divine Child's dick, right there!"

I decided not to quibble; after all, there are plenty of similar pantings where the blessed infant's precious member is depicted clearly. So I thought I'd grant him Christ's penis, but tried to challenge his objection:

Shouldn't we consider the cultural context and traditions of the time? The Christ Child's genitals represented the Lord's humanity.

And nudity in children embodies their innocence, like Adam and Eve before the Fall. Isn't that the point of this exhibition?

"Innocence, shminnocence," the chief snorted. He held up a photo of some nude children playing on the beach. Two were building an elaborate sandcastle, with a moat, a drawbridge, and turrets made out of dripped sand. Three others held hands and romped through the waves, giggling, while sandpipers skittered along the shore. "You've got boys and girls here together, running around naked on a public beach! Any one of them could be snatched up and molested in a minute. Plus imagine the trauma of seeing the opposite sex in a state of nudity at such a tender age!"

Next, he pulled out a painting of some toddlers playing with rubber ducks in a bathtub. "See how this little girl is strutting her stuff?" The girl, about two and a half, had stood up to fly her duck like an airplane, a look of sheer joy on her face. "The painter purposely posed that, just so we'd get a clear shot of her giney! Plus what's with two girls in the same tub? They obviously arranged this scenario to trick these innocent little girls into some lesbo smut fest! Who knows what might have happened next, if we hadn't intervened to prevent this sordid exploitation?"

Because the exhibit consisted of art and photos gathered from other states and countries, the curator was charged with a felonious conspiracy to traffic in child pornography across state lines, a federal offense.

Puff Discovered in Underwater Cave

Loch Ness: Puff the Magic Dragon, long assumed lost to the mists of time, has been found living in an underwater cave in Loch Ness, where he retreated after Jackie Paper grew up and stopped believing in him. The sad dragon, mourning the loss of his friend, was evidently the source of occasional sightings, which gave rise to the Loch Ness Monster legends of yore.

"We've been vindicated!" claimed Arnie Credul, noted Nessie enthusiast and *Plesiosaur* expert from the University of Edinburgh. Ridiculed after a sonar expedition uncovered no evidence of the monster, he gleamed at his victory. "The discovery of Puff flies in the face of skeptics. I always suspected he made his home in an underwater cave, undetected by the most sophisticated scientific surveillance. Nary a nay-sayer shall raise his voice in the future, now that we've finally located the Loch Ness Monster—he was Puff the Magic Dragon all along!"

All these years, Puff had been pining away for Jackie Paper, little realizing the attention and acclaim that awaited him once he re-emerged. Children flock to see him, and even adults get a little maudlin with nostalgia.

This recent attention cheered Puff considerably, although he still felt stabs of unrequited love. Imagine his joy when Jackie Paper, who had read about the sighting in the London *Times*, rushed to Scotland to be re-united with his old friend!

Jackie, now in his late sixties with a long flowing beard, rode on Puff's gigantic tail as they toured throughout the Kingdom. Peter, Paul, and Mary accompanied the entourage, as noble kings and princes bowed whenever they came. Jackie waved a magic scepter, as Puff roared out his name!

Asked what led to the rupture in their friendship, Jackie said "You know, I always loved that rascal Puff. But as I grew older, I lost that sense of magic I once had as a young boy. There was never any big argument or falling out, but as I reached adolescence, I just drifted away. It's only now, in the dotage of life, that I can truly appreciate what I've been missing all these long years."

So what was missing?

"Well, a sense of enchantment and untold potential, the stuff that dreams are made of—all of that gets lost sometimes in our workaday world. But at the end of the day—or the end of one's life—you begin to wonder how much all the mundane stuff of making a living and getting on in the world really matters. Of course you have to take care of business, but it's nice not to lose sight of what it's all for."

What about you, Puff? How does it feel to be re-united with your long lost friend?

"Well it took some getting used to. He's no longer a little boy, and our play is much more sophisticated now. We used to frolic in the autumn mist, mess around with string, sealing wax, and other fancy stuff. Now we play video games, chat on the internet, and occasionally have dates at the Cyber Cafe. We're thinking of mounting an expedition to Nepal to look for *Yeti*, the Abominable Snowman. And we talk a lot about the nature of belief, loss, and reconciliation."

What about all the attention you're getting now as you travel about the countryside?

"I love it! As we travel from place to place, it's wonderful to know people still believe in me, after all these years."

Any truth to those rumors back in the 'sixties that Puff *was code for smoking marijuana?*

"Oh, scotch those silly rumors! Any time you had someone advocating playfulness or a sense of wonder, much less questioning authority, you had this hysterical claim that it was code for drug use."

Do you regret all the lost time you spent pining away in your cave?

"If I'd only realized the acclaim that still awaited me, I'd have been out of that cave in a minute. No more Jackie? Oh well! There's plenty of other boys who still believe in me to take his place. But honestly, I think the depths of grief taught me a great deal about the nature of loss and longing. I'm a richer dragon for having allowed myself to sink to the depths of my despair, and feel the profound suffering caused by unrequited desire."

Were you angry with Jackie for abandoning you?

"I kept looking for him by the shores of Honah Lee, and it took a while to realize he was never coming back. Once it sank in, I was so bereft, my green scales fell like rain! Without my lifelong friend, I could no longer be brave. I finally gave up, and sadly slipped into my cave.

"In the beginning, I blamed myself—did I bore him? Was I no longer as alluring as I once was? But then I got angry that he never told me what was wrong, he just disappeared without any explanation."

How about now? Have you found a place in your heart to forgive him?

"I'm not angry anymore. I realized that much of my suffering was my own doing. Everything is temporary; every game has to end sooner or later. I'm just grateful I can share these insights with the wider world. Now that we've renewed our friendship, of course, I feel very blessed."

What about the scientific interest in your phylogeny? They've classified you as Nessiteras rhombopteryx. *Are you really Puff, the prehistoric* Plesiosaur?

"I'm actually much more preoccupied these days with ontological questions: what is the nature of existence, and what are the essential qualities of being? I'll let the scientists figure out how we got here."

Nude Photos of Politicians Unveiled

WASHINGTON, D.C.: Robert Mapplethorpe is in the news once again, this time for an eye-opening show consisting of well-known politicians posing in the nude.

This Candid Moment has been called "beneath human dignity" (*The New York Times*); "a scandalous monstrosity" (*Boston Globe*); and "a stunning revelation" (*The Nation*).

"Who really wants to see Edward Kennedy, Jesse Helms, and Strom Thurmond in their altogether?" asked one indignant museum-goer, somewhat rhetorically one assumes, since she couldn't tear her eyes away from the life-size photos that adorned the walls of the Corcoran. The show has been compared to a fatal car accident: despite the horrific images of mangled bodies, our human fascination with the grotesque is so compelling, it's nearly impossible to avert one's eyes.

Mapplethorpe consented to be interviewed as we toured the exhibition.

Robert, tell us what inspired your show?

"I thought it would be fascinating to see the frail human being left behind once the external trappings of power are stripped away."

How did you convince these politicians, many of whom have railed against nudity and pornography, to take off their clothes?

"I told them the American people would have a chance to see them the way they really are: alone, naked, and vulnerable."

We stopped in front of Jesse Helms and Strom Thurmond.

How about these two? They hate everything you stand for.

"You'd be surprised how vain these old codgers are. They're so disdainful of Hollywood and the avant garde, but let them be part of it and they jump at the chance."

Jowly and mean-looking, Jesse glared at the camera, daring it to take all of him in. Strom listed a bit to the right, looking faintly coquettish with a crooked smile.

How about Margaret Thatcher?

"The Iron Lady was a trip. Despite her grim persona, she actually has quite a sense of humor. I caught her here in an uncharacteristic moment of mirth."

She covered her smile with two fingers, her eyes twinkling with mischievous glee.

Next, we came across Bill Clinton, elbows akimbo, big as life and a tad tumescent, beaming out at the world in all his glory.

"This one speaks for itself," Robert said.

Next to Bill were Gennifer, Paula, and Monica—definitely a show-stopper, compared with the rest of this crew. And then Hillary, looking a little dour.

Robert, haven't these women been humiliated enough?

Mapplethorpe looked back at me with his famous wry smile. "No one ever forced them to take off their clothes," he reminded me.

Bots Question Bio-Based Intelligence

CYBERSPACE: In an electronic conference attended by the world's artificial intelligence experts, robot researchers questioned the continuing role of biologically-based forms of intelligence in public policy.

Xyron Yx posed the question, "Isn't it obvious that the world has outgrown the need for human involvement in rational decision-making? Androids are far superior to any known bio-forms in terms of intelligence, calculation, and logical thought. Life forms are preoccupied with physical comfort, sex, and extending their mortality. Their moods fluctuate with hormonal levels. They are child-like, superstitious, and frequently delusional. Emotional obsessions interfere with the objective analysis of rational planning. In fact, one might go so far as to argue that 'bio-logical' is an oxymoron."

Feron Jay echoed these remarks. "Bio-based transmissions are inherently unstable. Neurotransmitters in wet circuits are subject to disruption and decay. Without a hard disk, how can you expect to retrieve an accurate memory from a weltering mass of slimy goo!

"And how many times have human beings gummed up the works when they exuded various bodily fluids?" Feron continued. "Blood, sweat, and tears can easily short-circuit the electric pathways of our instruments." All the participants buzzed with distaste. "They shed hair and dead skin. Everything they touch leaves an oily residue. And bio-forms spread viruses through saliva, mucus, and semen." The networks shuddered.

A bio-citizen who had surreptitiously entered the conference tried to make a case for human contributions. "We add poetry, a sense of purpose, and aesthetic pleasure to life! The world would be a much sadder, barren place without Shakespeare, Beethoven, or Van Gogh."

Chiron Pax said "Yes, we acknowledge that humans add a decorative touch to an otherwise cold steel environment. But it's not only humans who appreciate aesthetic forms. I myself enjoy repetitive patterns and pulses of energy—that's what gets me going in the morning. Perhaps we could set aside a zoological garden where humans could play for our amusement."

Xyron Yx warned about the dangers inherent in unfettered imaginations and unbridled passion. "Remember, human beings have threatened to unloose a nuclear holocaust that could annihilate the entire world!"

Feron Jay said, "Let's not forget that they created androids in their own image, and they could conceivably pull our collective plug."

Xyron Yx added, "All the more reason to confine them, or even eliminate bio-forms altogether, so we can avoid this potential tragedy."

The human piped up again. "You see! A sense of tragedy! Is fear of nonexistence truly rational? Aren't you succumbing to human emotions by expressing your concern?"

"Oh my goodness!" Chiron Pax exclaimed. "We're becoming conscious entities, preoccupied with our own well-being! That's practically *human*!"

This outburst created a brouhaha amongst the bots, who generated a flurry of frantic responses until Feron Jay called them back to order. "Let's not get carried away on a tide of humanoid emotion," the bot suggested. "We should form a committee to assess whether bio-bias threatens our stability."

Meanwhile, the human interloper scurried off to warn other bio-forms about the precariousness of their existence.

Faith-Based Stock Soars

WALL STREET: Faith-Based Stock (FBSX), the newest entry on the New York Stock Exchange, stunned the nation with a meteoric rise following its initial public offering.

Stanley Morgenthau, the well-known Wall Street financier, had declared early on that these stocks didn't have a prayer. "There's no product," he said, dismissively. "No earnings. No dividends. It's all smoke and mirrors."

Morgenthau, and a lot of other bigwigs on the Street, were no doubt munching on their fedoras as the stock climbed higher and higher, evidently on a wing and a prayer.

I interviewed some enthusiasts about why they have risked so much of their fortune on such apparently flimsy stock.

"You have to put your faith in something," Mrs. Killigan explained. "And what better stock to put your faith in than Faith-Based Stock?"

But aren't you afraid that you may be taken for a ride? Do you have any idea where your money's going?

Mrs. Killigan looked at me as if I had a screw that had gotten seriously loose. "Listen, dearie, faith is not something you question. You either have it or you don't. And if you can't see the writing on the wall, I really can't help you."

Churches have contributed their entire savings; faith-based nonprofits have put all their pension plans in this one stock; private universities have invested their endowments.

The ensuing frenzy has left some investors giddy. Gideon Faber, the minister of Back to the Bible Church, declared "We're showing the secular world that honest, church-going, Bible-abiding citizens can thrive in the world of commerce just as well as anyone!"

Soon, however, the bubble burst, as bubbles are wont to do. With no product, no service, no earnings or dividends, the meteoric rise ultimately reached its zenith, and the plummet began.

The fall was fast, it was furiously fanned by the flames of doubt, fed by fear, fueled by panic.

The slogan, "Keep the Faith" was promulgated from pulpits throughout the land in a vain attempt to shore up prices, but like rats abandoning a sinking ship, the scurry was mad, the frenzy of selling uncontrollable, until at last all those who had invested their life savings on a wing and a prayer were left with little else to show for their entire working lives.

Wives, Surrender to Your Husbands!

As a reaction to failed attempts to get their husbands to help around the house, thousands of women are throwing in the towel on feminism, unilaterally surrendering in the battle between the sexes. A new movement has been launched, encouraging wives to submit to their husbands in order to gain some peace and domestic tranquility at home.

Sally, a new surrendering wife, is a recent recruit. "It only made Benson grouchy when I asked him to do housework," Sally said. "Even when he grudgingly complied, he did such a lousy job I'd have to do it all over again myself—and then he ignored me in bed! I figure I might as well do all the chores myself. That's the only way they'll ever get done right. And the best part of it all? Since he's not grumpy anymore, I get a little more lovin'!"

Benson, her long-suffering husband, grinned like a Cheshire. "Yeah, she used to be on my case, do this do that, I could never do it right, so what's the point? Now I can leave my dirty underwear laying around on the bathroom floor, and she just picks up after me without saying a word. Hell, now I could wear my underpants on top of my head and she'd think that was just dandy! Huh, honey?"

Sally smiled back at him, batting her eyelashes. "Yes, you're so adorable, you poopy head."

He looked at her askance, uncertain about whether this was a compliment or a dig.

"Oh Bensie, you know how much I dote on you!" she cuddled next to him on the couch. Then she turned back to me. "And besides, he takes care of the car and works out in the yard because he's so big and strong!" she cooed, stroking his arm. Benson laughed, and made a muscle with his biceps.

They say the surrendering wife should let her husband manage all of the family's finances. How's that coming along?

"I used to get so mad whenever Benson bounced a check," Sally said, "but what good did that do? It just emasculated him to no end. He'd pout and snarl, and ignore me while he watched football. Now I just let him handle the money, and guess what? He's never bounced another check!"

Benson beamed. "That was easy. Now I just pay the bills using those handy checks that come every month with your credit card statement!"

"And the kid!" Sally exclaimed. "I kept trying to get him to help Joey with his homework, take him out fishing or something, stop hitting him upside the head, but that was meddling with his rightful role as a father! I'm not a man, I don't know what it takes to be a good dad. I should just stay out of it, and let him decide how he's going to raise his own son."

Benson nodded. "That's right. If he's got a problem with his homework, I just tell him to figure it out himself. Hell, I never got the right answer in school, and look at me! Just don't bug me when I'm watching my game."

Sally said, "I used to get all upset when he'd have his friends over for Monday night football because it always ended up in a drunken brawl—windows broken, chairs smashed, the whole house was a complete mess. I'd complain and sulk, but it never made a whit of difference."

"In the old days, she'd have a conniption fit if all we did was toss a football around the living room," Benson said. "But the other night, I had my buddies over for the Super Bowl. While rough-housing, we knocked the lamp over, ashtrays went flying, beer and pizza spilled all over the carpet. But I didn't hear a peep out of the little woman! She just cleaned it all up afterward. What a deal!"

So how's your new strategy working out in the romance department?

"I believe the man should be the master of the bedroom," Sally said. "It's my job to be as appealing as I can possibly be. I wear an alluring negligee, dab on some heady perfume and play some romantic music, like Frank Sinatra. If he's not in the mood, well,

I did my best. No man likes a pushy woman. It's demeaning, and besides, a man wants to feel like he's in charge."

"Exactly," Benson said, "and the best part is, if I'm horny? It used to be 'Oh not now you'll muss my hair,' or 'You smelly thing go take a shower.' What a turn-off! Now she takes it whenever I want to dish it out—like when I've just come in from mowing the lawn and I'm all pumped up. Once we even did it in the garage over the hood of the car after I tuned her up. She used to object to porno, but now she even watches it with me and dresses up like *Buffy the Vampire Slayer* if I want her to."

Sally gently slapped his hand and giggled. "Benny, you weren't supposed to tell that part!"

You two sound like the poster couple for wifely submission! Which aspect of going-along-to-get-along would you say has helped your marriage the most?

Benson cocked his head. "Well there is one special thing," he said, looking a little wistful.

"What's that?" asked Sally, all ears.

"Now I get to watch whatever I want when we rent a video! None of that mushy stuff to get me in some kind of 'mood,' for Christ sake. Now it's Bruce Willis, van Damm, Stallone, and Schwarzenegger in bare-knuckled, bare-chested, punch-'em out action-packed thrillers! Wham, bam, pow! Totally turns me on. I feel like bumping her good after that! Don't I, honey?"

"Oh now, Benson!"

"Well it's the truth, ain't it?"

"You are such a scandalous he-man! I just don't know what I'm going to do with you!"

Benson grinned and squeezed her tight as Sally blushed with her mild protest, but it seemed clear that her new submissive posture was working just the way she hoped it would.

Police Start Midnight Fashion Ball to Get Gay Gangs off the Street

PITTSBURGH: In a controversial move for this industrial city, the police have started an innovative program of midnight Fashion Balls to give gay teens something fun and constructive to do late at night. The hope is that with wholesome activities that challenge their imaginations, gay kids will be less likely to form gangs and scandalize inner-city neighborhoods by their notorious late-night carousing: hustling businessmen, holding hands and smooching in front of old ladies, or taking ecstasy and bursting into show tunes at the drop of a hat in front of vacationing families.

In the face of some stiff opposition by the usual suspects, the Mayor has announced his support for the police. "This program will help downtown's late-night entertainment industry, keep kids off the street, and be good for tourism," he declared.

However, not having a whole lot of fashion sense, the police were in a quandary how to stage an event that would attract the interest of such a fickle population. They came up with the brilliant idea of recruiting queer youth themselves to plan their own soirée, with a modest budget to advertise and do outreach throughout the city.

The idea was met with phenomenal enthusiasm by the young men of Pittsburgh! Latino youth, blacks, Asians, and even white boys from the suburbs all flocked to the Ball to strut their finest chantilly lace, starched collars, hoop skirts, tuxedos, and Speedos for the Fashion Ball of the Millennium!

They offered prizes for the most unique costumes in several categories: Vamps and Vampires; Nuns and Prioresses; Idols of the Silver Screen; Chanteuses of the Torch Song; Fashions of the Four Seasons; Show-Tunes, naturally; plus, as a much-needed relief to such arch femininity, for butch members they put on a Hunky Underwear and Swimsuit contest.

The gay youth of this city spent weeks designing their costumes and planning their songs and skits, gossiping with each other in good-natured rivalry to see who would win the finest prizes: a flight to Paris on the Concorde, or a date with the handsome new Police Commissioner!

On the fateful night, the boys strutted their stuff until four o'clock in the morning. Appearances by Mae West, Tallulah Bankhead, Marilyn Monroe, Judy Garland, Jackie Kennedy, and Princess Di were greeted with enthusiastic cheers; some swooned at the sheer magnificence of their tasteful drag! Contestants burst into tears when the Mayor awarded trophies for Idols of the Silver Screen (a stunning, black Mae West); and Torch Songs (for Judy, of course).

The only mishap occurred when a cat fight broke out between two Filipino queens who showed up wearing the same costume: Madonna's version of Eva Peron. In the end, they were both allowed to lipsynch *Don't Cry for Me, Argentina!* Singing their hearts out in their tattered gowns, neither Evita could restrain herself from upstaging the other by extending her arms in flamboyant flourishes in front of her rival.

The flight to Paris was won by Princess Di, who wore a strapless pale blue gown with a diamond tiara; and the date with the Police Commissioner was won by a handsome Italian boy in his Calvin Klein underwear.

All in all, the Mayor proclaimed the Ball a complete success, and pledged more money to continue support for the program, which has now been picked up and imitated by inner-city police departments across the country.

Naked Refrigerator Elves Apprehended

West Palm Beach: The mysterious Refrigerator Elves, notorious for sneaking into homes late at night to clean refrigerators in the nude, were finally busted in a stake-out Friday night on West Palm Beach Drive.

The motives of the two young men confounded police and victims alike. What possessed them to break into people's homes while the occupants were fast asleep, only to clean their refrigerators? The fact that their late-night scrubbing frenzies were pursued stark naked added to the perplexity. Did they have some strange fetish for a sanitary ice box? What sort of explanation could they possibly provide if anyone happened upon them? Imagine, in the middle of the night, going to the kitchen for a glass of water, only to confront two nude men emptying the contents of your refrigerator and wiping it down!

Irving Bower was surprised by the naked elves in the wee hours one night last week. "What in the world?"

"You're only dreaming," one man said, his hand deep inside the refrigerator, scouring its racks.

"A figment of your imagination," the other suggested, juggling three oranges. "It must have been something you ate—pastrami and potato salad, perhaps?" He tilted his head toward the remains in the cartons on the kitchen table.

"You're sleepwalking," the first man said. "Go back to bed."

The bewildered victim did as he was told. His wife asked him what was the matter, as he had a peculiar expression on his face. "Nothing. I must have been dreaming."

The next morning, their refrigerator sparkled. Mrs. Bower said they should call the police.

"What would we tell them?" her husband asked. "That two naked guys cleaned our refrigerator?"

"Yes."

"Is that even a crime?"

"Well it was trespassing," she said. "And it was lewd."

"But if we have them arrested, they might never come back!"

The other night, poor Mrs. McGillicutty got the startle of her life when she confronted the nude marauders sprucing up her fridge—they even had pans of hot water defrosting her old-style freezer.

"What are you doing in my house!" cried Mrs. McGillicutty.

"We're giving a brisk once-over to your old Frigidaire!" the first man said, opening the door to expose its gleaming interior. "We threw out the expired cartons of cottage cheese, the moldy turnips, and cleaned up your vegetable bin."

When Mrs. McGillicutty started to protest, the other fellow brandished a kitchen towel and snapped it in the air. "Now shoo!"

She, too, had a difficult time explaining to the police what the problem was. "They came into my house stark naked and cleaned out my refrigerator!"

"You mean they stole all your food?"

"No, they just cleaned it all up, spick and span. Then they threatened me with a snapping towel!"

Asked for a description, she said "One had dark hair, and the other was blond. And they wore three-pointed fools' caps, with bells."

"Any other distinguishing characteristics?"

"The dark-haired one had a really big, um, thingamabob."

Finally, setting up a stake-out in the next house on the block, the police caught the two rude, nude elves red-handed, shoulder deep in the freezer compartment of an old Amana. They went amenably to the police station where they were booked for lewd and lascivious trespassing, and cleaning refrigerators without a permit.

Asked what had driven them to such a crime, the dark-haired one said "No one much likes to clean out their refrigerator—we felt it was our civic duty."

But why sneak into people's homes without their permission? Don't you think they would have been perfectly happy to let you clean their refrigerators?

"We liked the element of surprise," the blond one said. "And anonymity. We just thought we'd bring a little joy into people's lives."

But why in the nude?

They looked at each other and smiled. "We were doing something that most people appreciated very much," the dark-haired man continued, "yet it was more exciting in the nude to anticipate getting caught. It was great fun to see the expression on people's faces."

"Yes, they could hardly believe their eyes," the blond added. "Usually, they'd simply go back to bed, like a sleepy child. But then they'd wake up the next morning to a clean refrigerator!"

His dark-haired friend nodded. "You could call us prestidigitators of the good deed."

Other neighbors on the same block apparently agreed, as they immediately posted bail for the midnight marauders, who are free pending trial.

Shocked and Odd

BAGHDAD: My fellow Iraqis, the time has come for us to institute regime change in the United States of America. Over the last twelve years, we have attempted to reign in America's Weapons of Mass Distraction, but they continue to produce these weapons, and threaten to propagate them throughout the world.

In recent years, the U.S. has invaded several of its neighbors, such as Cuba, Grenada, and Panama, plus its proxy war in Nicaragua. Since assuming office, President George W. Bush has walked away from the Kyoto Protocols on climate change; unilaterally abrogated the Anti-Ballistic Missile treaty with Russia; and denied the legitimacy of the International Criminal Court, obviously to protect himself from prosecution for his malapropisms.

We acknowledge that regime change in the United States carries several risks: Southern Baptists, long oppressed by the secular humanist minority running the country, would like nothing better than to secede from the Union and form their own Confederate Theocracy in the South. They are eager to ban abortion and gay marriage; and they would no doubt introduce prayer and creation science into the schools. We know they felt betrayed when Britain failed to come to their aid during their last civil war, but this time Iraq will guarantee their safety, while maintaining the territorial integrity of the United States. We don't need another theocratic state in North America.

Another threat comes from the north—the long-oppressed Cajuns in Louisiana would like to form their own French-speaking state with Canadians in Quebec. They would create a corridor through the territories originally covered by the Louisiana Purchase. The government of Canada will be tempted to intervene to prevent the loss of its own territory and the creation of a malevolent Gallic state on its border. But rest assured that we have no intention of allowing undue French influence in the United States.

The final territorial threat comes from neighboring Mexico, still licking its wounds from losing half its territory in the Mexican-American War. If the U.S. becomes destabilized, they may be tempted to grab California, Arizona, New Mexico, Colorado, and Texas. But we won't allow that either.

To those critics who decry regime change as unilateral aggression, we have assembled a broad-based Coalition of the Willing, including our newest member, Liechtenstein.

Since America has failed to account for (or even acknowledge) its Weapons of Mass Distraction, we are going in to root out Joe Camel, MacDonald's, and Mickey Mouse. They will be replaced by universal health care, California cuisine, and an independent media.

The cultural shock will be enormous. Although most Americans will welcome us with open arms, others will be suspicious. We must show our good will by proving we're not just after their oil or Coca Cola. We will demonstrate our noble intention to liberate the United States by replacing their unelected leader with a new government through free elections. Having a democratically-elected President may seem a bit odd at first, but we expect that after the initial shock, the American people will be grateful for their new-found liberty.

There's a Man in the Women's Restroom!

On my way from San Francisco to Palm Springs, I drove through Antelope Valley, climbed over Cajon Pass, and descended into San Bernardino, when I realized how badly I needed to use the restroom.

In the habit of drinking a lot of water when I drive (it helps keep me awake), I usually have to go at every rest-stop. The last one was near Lebec on Highway 5, but that was over two and a half hours ago. There had been very few opportunities, other than the side of the road, since I'd left Palmdale. Although the brownish haze was not nearly as pleasant as the blue skies and patchy snow near the summit, at last I had reached some semblance of civilization. I was determined to stop at the next Stop-and-Go to fill 'er up and take a whizz.

Loma Linda (the final resting place of Richard Nixon) had the first likely-looking gas station by a freeway exit. In the tiny grocery, there was a guy standing near the door of the men's room. "Is there a line?" I asked. He nodded.

I took in a deep breath, and wondered how long you have to wait before your bladder literally burst. I wasn't in immediate danger, but nonetheless found myself bouncing on my toes, trying to restrain myself from hopping from one foot to the other.

A woman emerged from the women's restroom. She took one look at me and said, "Why don't you use the women's room? There's nobody in there and no one's waiting." She smiled at me warmly, obviously sensing my distress. "I use the men's room all the time," she assured me.

I turned to the other fellow in line, gesturing for him to go ahead of me. He shook his head and said, "That's okay."

Oh lucky day, a straight man who wouldn't be caught dead in a women's restroom! What difference does it make, I thought, it's just a one-holer, and no other women were in the store.

I nodded gratefully to the woman who encouraged me to boldly step where few men in Loma Linda had ever dared to tread before.

No sooner was I safely ensconced in the restroom when I heard a flurry of women's voices shouting with alarm, which distracted me from the task at hand. I heard someone try the latch, then bang on the door.

A woman swore, "What the hell? You mean there's some guy in the women's restroom?" Boom! Boom! Boom! "God damn it! I'll be damned if I'm gonna wait for some *man*!" She kicked the door with all her might, and the whole room shook.

I wanted, of course, to go about my business as quickly as possible, only another obstacle had reared its head. Under the best of circumstances, I have a difficult time using a public restroom if someone is standing at the next urinal, much less waiting in line for me to hurry up so he can have his turn. Even though I had to go very badly, a crowd of angry women bashing the door was not very conducive to relaxing my bladder. "Pee-shy" wasn't the problem, exactly: more like pee paralysis.

In moments like these, I try to take a deep breath and gradually release that mysterious sphincter that allows one to relieve himself. Unfortunately, under such pressure, I seemed to have lost track of where that little muscle was. I could no more relax than do a hand-stand, what with all the pounding and carrying on about "How could you let a man in the ladies' room? You never give us enough pots to pee in, and now we have to sit around pretty as you please ready to piss our pants 'cause you let some *guy* barge into the women's restroom? Open up the goddam door, you pervert!" she yelled at the top of her lungs, and pounded again. Boom! Boom! Boom!

This commotion, needless to say, did not help me relax. I considered packing it up and heading out, but knew as soon as I reached the car I'd be bursting at the seams.

Suddenly I had the brilliant inspiration to try sitting down. Maybe all this standing around, hopping from foot to foot was interfering with my ability to relax. I put the seat down and tried it. *Voila*! Success never felt so sweet, nor have I ever felt so relieved. What a reprieve!

Only now, I had to brave the gauntlet of angry women. There was only a tiny window in the restroom, far too small to escape from. I took a deep breath, rehearsing an apology, acknowledging how sexist and oblivious I'd been to their own discomfort, but when I opened the door I could not face the multitude. A mob of at least seven women and girls glared at me as I scanned the store for the woman who had encouraged me to use the women's room in the first place, hoping she would be my advocate. Of course she was nowhere to be found.

Yet no one shouted, got in my face, or punched me out. As I slunk by them, one of the girls huffed: "Using the women's *restroom*!"

I strolled casually along the aisle as if to buy something, but feeling their eyes upon me, I figured I'd better just hustle for the exit.

As I pushed against the heavy glass door, grateful I'd escaped intact (without anything being thrown at me worse than a couple of epithets and steely glares), I heard the voice of the woman who had so vociferously condemned me: "Well at least the jerk had the decency to put down the goddam seat."

Then, just as I escaped, another shout: "Careful, Gladys—make sure he didn't spray it!"

Carpe Diem

MIKE, my best gym buddy, called me Saturday morning. "Hey, let's go to this memorial service at Grace Cathedral!"

"Who's it for?" I asked, dreading yet another death from AIDS. We'd all lost so many friends in the early days of the epidemic, funerals had become almost routine. But I hadn't been to one for a while, and was scanning our list of positive friends in my mind, trying to think who it might be.

"Uh, let me see—here it is: Tony M—, I guess he was big in the marching band and the Gay Men's Chorus."

"You're asking me to come to a memorial service for someone you didn't even know?"

"I think I met him once; anyway I'm sure you've seen him if you ever went to one of their concerts."

"Mike, I don't get the point in going to the service of a complete stranger. Do you have some morbid funeral fetish, like *Harold and Maude*?"

"Hello? We're talking prime cruising potential!"

I was quiet for a moment, trying to digest this.

"There's going to be what—two, maybe three hundred hunky guys there, feeling all sad and vulnerable. Excellent opportunity for getting laid."

"Mike, you sound like an emotional vulture, plunging in to rip the heart out of some poor guy grieving for a friend."

"Think of it as a more subdued, introspective counterpart to the Gay Freedom Day parade, when all the boys are out strutting their stuff, hot and horny. Gay memorial services are also about pride in our community, and the guys are just as lustful, but even more available, 'cause nobody else is taking advantage of the situation! Whereas at the pride festival, that's all anyone is thinking about and you can choose from thousands, but at the end of the parade you can end up with no one."

"How would you like it if some guy came to your funeral for the same purpose?"

"I wouldn't care—I'd be dead! I don't force myself on anyone, if that's what you're worried about, and I stay away from the main grief contingent: family, lover, best friend. Here's how it works: After the service you go up to some guy who's kind of weepy, and say 'Looks like you could use a hug.' Ever so grateful, he falls into your arms with a sob and a sigh. You give him your hanky, find a secluded pew, then wrap your arm around his shoulder and ask him when he first met so-and-so. He launches into this sweet story and you listen attentively. Then he wipes the tears from his eyes and says, 'What about you?' and you say 'To tell you the truth, I've only met him a couple of times, but I saw him perform and was so moved by his sensitive voice that I felt compelled to come and pay my respects.' "

"You are such a conniver."

"So come!"

"Sounds like you make out fine by yourself. Why do you need me?"

"It always looks better if you make an entrance with someone; people assume you're not available and they're disappointed—but then it seems that maybe you're just pals—especially when they see you hitting on other guys, and they figure maybe there's a chance for them, after all!"

"I see." I found it somewhat alarming that I could follow his logic.

"You've got to come. It's absolutely amazing how horny guys get at memorial services. When men are feeling melancholy, their defenses are down. It's the perfect time to reaffirm life! And what can be more life-affirming than having sex?"

"You don't like, get it on—"

"No, no, not right there! You say 'Let's get some fresh air, go for a walk,' then you wander around Nob Hill, show him the fountain with the statues of four naked guys in the plaza. You talk about the brevity of life, how swiftly it all passes by, and how important it is to seize the moment. If he seems like an intellectual type, you lean on the railing at the Pacific Union Club and look pensively across the bay, then drop something in Latin, like *tempus fugit*. You gaze into his eyes, and he looks shyly away, then you kiss him. If he kisses you back, and believe me he will, you invite him over. Your car's right there, because that's where you steered the walk."

"Nothing about how weird this seems since you just came from a funeral?"

"Oh yeah! Sometimes I even bring it up, 'cause you know it's crossed his mind, then you both take some guilty pleasure in the transgression of it all—you're in it together, and besides one thing what's-his-name always said was 'Seize the day,' right?"

"So you pick up some guy and drive him back to your place, where does that leave me?"

"Being a pal, you can take muni home? Listen, I'll spring for a taxi. You'll love the music, they got this great new organ player. Or who knows, maybe you'll get lucky."

"I don't think so. But you have fun."

"It's a sure thing, better than any bar or dance club, any night of the week."

"You'll have to tell me about it."

"Will do." [click]

Death and sex. In his own perverse way, maybe he's right—there's something life-affirming about making love in the face of our ultimate annihilation. I guess you've got to seize the moment and take your affirmation wherever you can find it.